Issued under the authority of

Manual
Firemanship

CW00674000

A survey of the science of fire-fighting

Book 3
Hand pumps, extinguishers and foam equipment

LONDON: HMSO

The structure and publishing history of
the *Manual* are shown on pages 99–102

ISBN 0 11 340626 6

Preface

In this Book equipment which is mainly portable is described. This ranges from hand-pumps, extinguishers and fire blankets to the types of equipment and extinguishing media used in the application of foam.

Part 1 is short, dealing with the few hand-pumps which are part of the standard brigade equipment and are generally useful in dealing with minor fires.

Part 2 describes some of the numerous types of portable extinguishers that have been developed for the various classes of small fires. A short chapter on fire blankets is also included.

Part 3 passes to the wide range of foams and foam-making equipment now available, which are generally used to extinguish hydrocarbon fires. This particular area has seen a rapid development in specialised media and methods of applying them.

Reference in this book to the male person should be construed as applying, as appropriate, to the female person also. The ranks of junior firewoman, firewoman and leading firewoman have been introduced by the Fire Services (Appointments and Promotion) (Amendment) Regulations 1976 to equate with the ranks of junior fireman, fireman, and leading fireman, and references to the latter should, where appropriate, be construed as references to the former.

The Home Office is indebted to all those who have assisted in the preparation of this work.

Home Office
1988

Guide to SI units

Quantity and basic or derived SI unit and symbol	Approved unit of measurement	Conversion factor
Length metre (m)	kilometre (km) metre (m) millimetre (mm)	1 km = 0.621 mile 1 m = 1.093 yards = 3.279 feet 1 mm = 0.039 inch
Area square metre (m^2)	square kilometre (km^2) square metre (m^2) square millimetre (mm^2)	1 km^2 = 0.386 $mile^2$ 1 m^2 = 1.196 $yards^2$ = 10.764 $feet^2$ 1 mm^2 = 0.002 $inch^2$
Volume cubic metre (m^3)	cubic metre (m^3) litre (l) ($= 10^{-3}$ m^3)	1 m^3 = 35.7 $feet^3$ 1 litre = 0.22 gallon
Volume, flow cubic metre per second (m^3/s)	cubic metre per second (m^3/s) litres per minute (l/min)	1 m^3/s = 35.7 $feet^3$/s 1 l/min = 0.22 gall/min
Mass kilogram (kg)	kilogram (kg) tonne (t)	1 kg = 2.205 lbs 1 t = 0.984 ton

Velocity
metre per second (m/s)
	metre per second (m/s)
	international knot (kn)
	  (= 1.852 km/h)
	kilometre per hour
	  (km/h)
		1 m/s = 3.281 feet/second
		1 km/h = 0.621 mile/hour

Acceleration metre per $second^2$ (m/s^2)	metre/$second^2$ (m/s^2)	1 m/s^2 = 3.281 feet/$second^2$ = 0.102 'g'
Force newton (N)	kilonewton (kN) newton (n)	1 kN = 0.1 ton force 1 N = 0.225 lb force

Quantity and basic or derived SI unit and symbol	Approved unit of measurement	Conversion factor
Energy, work joule (J) (= 1 Nm)	joule (J) kilojoule (kJ) kilowatt/hour (kW/h)	1 kJ = 0.953 British Thermal Unit 1 J = 0.738 foot lb force
Power watt (W) (= 1 J/s = 1 Nm/s)	kilowatt (kW) watt (W)	1 kW = 1.34 horsepower 1 W = 0.735 foot lb force/second
Pressure newton/metre^2 (N/m^2)	bar (= 10^5 N/m^2) millibar (mbar) (= 10^2 N/m^2) metrehead (= 0.0981 bar)	1 bar = 0.991 atmosphere = 14.5 lb force/in^2 1 mbar = 0.0288 inch Hg 1 metrehead = 3.28 foot head
Heat, quantity of heat joule (J)	joule (J) kilojoule (kJ)	1 kJ = 0.953 British Thermal Unit
Heat flow rate watt	watt (W) kilowatt (kW)	1 W = 3.41 British Thermal Units/hour 1 kW = 0.953 British Thermal Unit/second
Specific energy, calorific value, specific latent heat joule/kilogram (J/kg) joule/m^3 (J/m^3)	kilojoule/kilogram (kJ/kg) kilojoule/m^3 (kJ/m^3) megajoule/m^3 (MJ/m^3)	1 kJ/kg = 0.43 British Thermal Unit/lb 1 kJ/m^3 = 0.0268 British Thermal Unit/ft^3
Temperature degree Celsius (°C)	degree Celsius (°C)	1 degree Celsius = 1 degree Centigrade

Contents

Part 1
Hand-operated pumps

Part 2
Portable fire extinguishers and fire blankets

Chapter 3 Water-type extinguishers

Chapter 4 Foam extinguishers

Chapter 5 Powder extinguishers

Chapter 6 Halon extinguishers

Chapter 7 Carbon dioxide extinguishers

Chapter 8 Fire blankets

Part 3
Foam and foam-making equipment

Chapter 11 Operational use of foam

List of Plates

1 Chubb 'Slimjet' portable foam monitor.
Photo: County of Avon Fire Brigade.

2 The foam monitor of a Gloster Javelin airport foam tender.
Photo: Gloster Saro Limited.

3 Angus Mini-Turbex high expansion foam generator.
Photo: Angus Fire Armour Limited.

4 Galena 'Fog Foam' hose-reel foam unit.
Photo: Galena (Fire Engineering) Limited.

5 An example of a distribution manifold for use with a pressurised foam concentrate supply.
Photo: County of Avon Fire Brigade.

6 Part of a typical foam tender, showing various items of
equipment including LX foam branchpipes, inline inductors,
monitors and a Mobrey constaflo metering valve.
Photo: Cleveland County Fire Brigade.

7 A demountable-pod foam system.
Photo: County of Avon Fire Brigade.

8 Another version of a demountable-pod foam system, including a foam tank, foam branchpipe, monitor, and high expansion foam generator.
Photo: West Midlands Fire Service.

9 Another view of the pod system shown in Plate 8.
Photo: West Midlands Fire Service.

10 A foam tank trailer unit with a capacity of 28 000 litres of
foam concentrate.
Photo: County of Avon Fire Brigade.

11 The application of foam onto a crashed tanker train carrying
gas oil.
Photo: Greater Manchester County Fire Service.

Part 1
Hand-operated pumps

Introduction

The hand-pump is probably the oldest design of fire extinguishing machine. As a means of dealing with minor fires requiring only limited supplies of water, the pumps described are all simple and easy to use and require only one operator. They are often employed in extinguishing chimney or hearth fires, and one or other of the types will be found on most pumping appliances.

Natural resource planning

Introduction

Chapter 1
Hand-operated pumps

1 The hand pump

a. Construction

Prior to the introduction of the stirrup pump a small hand pump formed part of the standard equipment of most fire appliances. Very little alteration has been made in its design for many years past and, although superseded by the stirrup pump, the following detail is given to explain the principle used.

A typical example (Fig. 1.1) is single-acting, having one inlet

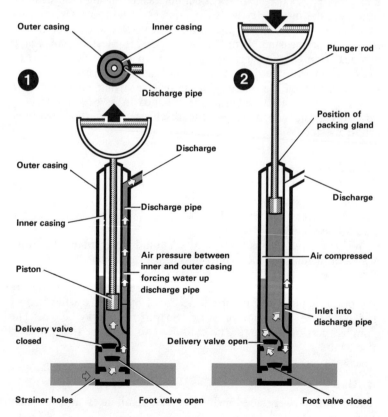

Fig. 1.1 Sections through a typical hand pump showing (1) valve positions on the upstroke, and (2) on the downstroke.

or foot valve and one delivery valve. It has a double casing, the space between the inner and outer casings serving as an air-pressure chamber to smooth out the pulsating action of the piston. The piston is formed from two leather cup washers secured to the end of the plunger rod by means of a nut.

Water is expelled through a discharge pipe which is connected to the upper or lower end of the outer casing. This discharge pipe has a male screw thread to which is connected one or more lengths of 15 mm rubber-lined canvas delivery hose. A 4.5 mm nozzle is fitted to the end of the hose which throws a jet to a height of about 9 metres. These pumps must be held in the water when pumping and to facilitate operation they are sometimes fitted with a stirrup similar to that employed on the stirrup type hand pump.

b. Operation

When the piston moves upwards (Fig.1.1 (1)) the foot valve opens and water enters the barrel of the inner casing through the strainer holes. As the piston descends (Fig. 1.1 (2)), the foot valve closes, the delivery valve opens and water flows from the inner barrel into the outer casing. From the outer casing most of this water escapes through the discharge pipe, but a certain quantity rises higher than the opening of this pipe and compresses the air in the upper part of the casing. On the reverse stroke when the inner casing is being recharged, this air expands to its original volume and forces the water out of the discharge pipe, thus giving a relatively steady jet.

c. Maintenance

To dismantle the pump, the packing gland is unscrewed and the piston is withdrawn from the cylinder. Access to the inlet and delivery valves is obtained by unscrewing the strainer box at the base of the pump.

When the pump has been used it should be dismantled and all water drained from the cylinder by pressing up on the spindle of the delivery valve. The whole pump should be cleaned and the leather piston washers well greased to ensure easy working. Before the pump is put away it should be tested by placing a finger over the discharge pipe and pressing the piston sharply down. The compression of the air in the cylinder should cause the piston to rise again.

d. Use

These pumps were used primarily for small fires and chimney fires.

2 The stirrup pump

a. Construction

To meet the danger of the large number of fires which were likely to be started by incendiary bombs in World War II, the Government decided to provide in large numbers a small hand pump which was simple in operation and would not break down in the hands of inexperienced operators. It was necessary, therefore, to produce a pump which had as few moving parts as possible, and avoided incorporating any parts which would be subject to wear when put to continual use. The factor governing the size of the pump is its primary use, i.e., the extinction of small fires using the minimum of water.

A typical design of a stirrup pump is shown in Fig. 1.2 (1) operating on the bucket and plunger principle (see the *Manual,* Book 7 Chapter 9), in which there are only three moving parts:

(i)   the plunger rod;

(ii) a ball which forms the foot valve;

(iii) a ball which forms a non-return valve in the piston at the base of the plunger rod.

The only part of the pump which is subjected to any appreciable wear is the packing of the gland at the top of the pump casing. This packing usually consists of graphited hemp or cotton, but if a leakage occurs at this point which cannot be remedied by tightening the gland nut, it is possible to improvise a packing with a piece of oiled or greased string.

At the top of the pump casing is an outlet which is connected to a 7.5 to 9-metre length of 12.5 mm bore rubber tubing to the end of which a nozzle is fixed. The nozzle originally provided was a dual-purpose one which was readily converted by a simple slide mechanism to give either a jet or a spray. In one position it would throw a 3 mm jet approximately 9 metres, and in the other a fine spray approximately 4.5 metres. This nozzle, however, has now been superseded by one giving a jet only. A stirrup is attached to the pump and when not in use the hose is coiled and secured by a strap.

b. Operation

The hose is uncoiled and the pump casing is placed in a bucket of water or other suitable container with the stirrup on the ground. The operator holds the pump in position by placing his foot on the stirrup and proceeds to pump. To obtain a solid stream of water and to avoid the pulsating effect which is noticeable with this type of pump, it is recommended that short quick strokes be used instead of the long slow ones which are used when operating, for example, a car tyre pump. This normal rate when using the jet is about 70 double strokes a minute which gives a delivery of

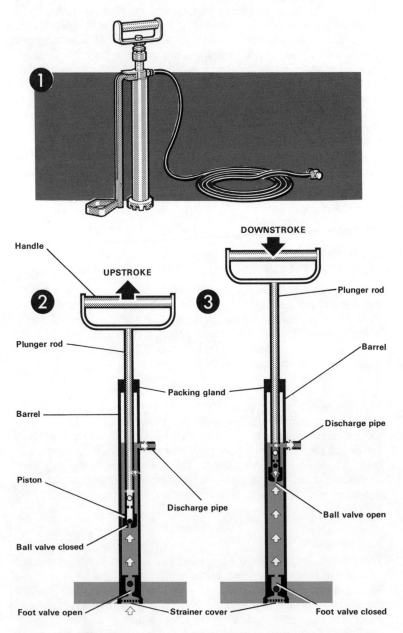

Fig. 1.2 (1) General view of a stirrup pump. (2 and 3) Section through the pump showing the path of water: (2) upstroke; (3) downstroke.

4.5 to 5.5 litres of water per minute. The internal working of the pump is shown in Fig. 1.2 (2 and 3).

When the plunger rod and the piston attached to the plunger rod move upwards (Fig. 1.2 (2)), the foot valve opens and water enters the barrel through the strainer cover; at the same time the ball valve in the piston closes and any water above the piston in the working barrel flows out through the discharge pipe. On the downward stroke (Fig. 1.2 (3)), the foot valve closes, the ball valve in the piston opens and a quantity of water enters the upper part of the working barrel, part of which is forced into the discharge pipe, the amount being equal to the displacement caused by the plunger rod.

c. Maintenance

If the pump fails to deliver water this will generally be due to one of three causes:

(i)   a choked strainer cover;

(ii)   ball valves seated in through lack of use;

(iii) a choked nozzle.

A choked strainer cover can be cleared by removing the pump from the water and scraping away any dirt which has accumulated. This is a common fault when the pump is operated from dirty water, and care should be taken to see that all buckets used in conjunction with stirrup pumps are free from such articles as cigarette ends, leaves, etc. The ball valve sometimes becomes stuck to the seat through lack of use. This can often be remedied by turning the pump upside down and pushing a pin or piece of wire through the gauze filter. If the ball is too firmly fixed, the strainer should be removed and the ball levered up with a thin stick. If this fails to dislodge the stuck ball, the pump must be dismantled.

Originally the balls were made of bronze, but during World War II, owing to a shortage of copper, plated steel balls were used. The plating, however, tended to chip and the balls rusted, thus rendering the valve inoperative. Nowadays, nylon balls are widely used. Choked nozzles can be cleared by unscrewing the nozzle and removing any dirt which has collected behind the jet or spray holes.

After the pump has been examined for the above faults, it should be subjected to a short pressure test by getting the pump to work. This will show whether the connections between the pump and the hose, and the hose and the nozzle, are satisfactory. Any signs of a leakage at these points should be rectified by tightening the collars or retying the wire. If water oozes from the gland at the top of the barrel this may be remedied by:

(i)   screwing down the collar until the leak ceases; or

(ii)   replacing the packing.

d. Use

Regular use of stirrup pumps is beneficial, but they should not be used with liquids such as disinfectant fluids, creosote or whitewash which might set up corrosion inside the pump or perish the rubber hose. These pumps can be used to extinguish any small fire for which water is suitable.

3 Bucket-mounted pump

a. Construction

The bucket-mounted pump consists of a single or double-acting pump, fitted with a suitable length of hose with nozzle, rigidly mounted in a metal water container having a capacity of about 9 to 13.5 litres, though larger sizes may sometimes be found. The pump is usually similar in general construction to the hand pump or the stirrup hand pump already described. The water container may be of copper or heavily galvanised iron.

b. Operation

The container is filled with water through the filler hole and the pump is operated in the normal manner, one man operating the pump, one man taking the hose and nozzle and one man replenishing the water as necessary. In the case of a small fire requiring only a small quantity of water, one man alone can operate the device holding the nozzle in one hand and pumping with the other.

c. Maintenance

This is the same as for the appropriate type of hand pump, but the container should be cleaned out and dried after use to prevent the onset of rusting or corrosion.

d. Use

These pumps are employed in the same manner as the other types of hand pump; they are not, however, widely used by fire brigades. Their principal advantage is stability in operation with reduced likelihood of upsetting the bucket whilst at work. Their disadvantage is size and the fact that either the container must be filled at the nearest water supply and then carried to where it is wanted, or water must be brought up in separate buckets.

4 Semi-rotary pump

a. Construction

Semi-rotary pumps are not part of normal fire-fighting equipment, but are more generally used for pumping liquids from one container into another. Since firemen may encounter them at some incidents, they are briefly described below. The semi-rotary pump is a self-priming pump and owing to its design characteristics, it is particularly useful for pumping liquids where large quantities under low heads are involved. Typical examples of such use are as bilge pumps or for extracting petrol from an underground tank.

These pumps are sturdily constructed, having a cast-iron body with metal (usually brass or bronze) clack valves and are operated by moving a handle attached to the central spindle backwards and forwards.

In the double-acting type (Fig. 1.3), the only moving parts are four clack valves and the wings which are attached to the central spindle. In effect these wings act like a piston, their outer edges being ground so as to make a watertight connection with the inner wall of the pump casing. The inlet at the base of the pump is screwed to take standard sizes of galvanised water tubing and particular attention should be paid to seeing that an airtight connection is made when installing the pump.

b. Operation

When the wing (Fig. 1.3, left) containing the clack valve (1) rises this valve is closed while the inlet clack valve (2) opens and water

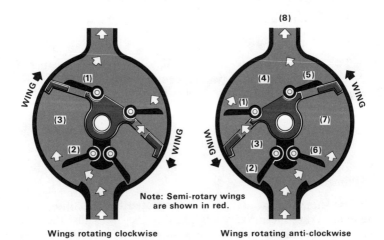

Note: Semi-rotary wings are shown in red.

Wings rotating clockwise   Wings rotating anti-clockwise

Fig. 1.3 Section through a double-acting type semi-rotary pump.

enters the pump casing (3). On the return stroke (Fig. 1.3, right) valve (1) opens, valve (2) closes and the water passes into the outlet chamber (4). At the same time the wing containing valve (5) rises, the other inlet valve (6) opens and water enters the pump casing (7). On each subsequent stroke the water in either (3) or (7) is expelled into the outlet chamber (4) and thence through the discharge pipe (8).

5 General

Hand pumps, a term which will for this chapter, include stirrup pumps, form a valuable part of fire-fighting equipment. Their principal advantages are:

(i)   They are light in weight, easily portable, and the person attacking the fire has only a light nozzle to handle.

(ii)   Provided a supply of water is available they can be got to work with considerable speed.

(iii) The jet can be maintained for as long as desired (unlike the portable extinguisher) and can be turned on or off at will.

(iv)   Plain water is used as an extinguishing medium and consequently damage to goods is less than when using liquids charged with chemicals.

(v)   The initial cost is low, they are simple in construction and operation, and, provided they are inspected and tested regularly, are very free from breakdown.

(vi)   The person pumping is clear of heat and smoke.

The disadvantages are:

(vii) Two and preferably three people are required to operate them, although one person can use the stirrup type of pump if adequate water supplies are available within striking distance of the fire.

(viii) A supply of water in buckets must be available or arrangements must be made to carry a portable supply.

(ix)   The physical exertion involved in pumping for any length of time is considerable.

In use these pumps are generally operated by a crew of three, one man taking the nozzle and attacking the fire whilst the other two remain with the pump, one pumping and the other feeding the pump with water. These two change over duties as the man on the pump becomes tired.

Hand pumps are of particular value in dealing with small fires of all types for which water is suitable, especially in their incipient stages. They are of particular value in the case of chimney fires.

Hand pumps should, as far as possible, be stored away from frost and out of the direct rays of the sun. The former will freeze up the valve and working parts unless the pump has been most carefully drained, whilst the direct rays of the sun have a deleterious effect on the rubber of the hose. When making up stirrup pumps care should be taken to coil the hose neatly, avoiding kinks and sudden bends which might cause the rubber to take a permanent set, to crack or to perish. Rubber hose and canvas hose for hand pumps should be cared for in precisely the same way as ordinary delivery hose.

6 Standard tests

All hand and stirrup pumps should be examined and tested at the times stipulated and in accordance with the *Fire Service Drill Book*.

Part 2
Portable fire extinguishers and fire blankets

Introduction

Although there are still a number of the old types of extinguisher which expel the extinguishing medium by a chemical reaction or by a self-contained hand-pump, these are being rapidly superseded by types using an internal charge of pressurised gas. The latter are generally more efficient, less damaging to materials and easier to refurbish, and they are described in this Part. One or two recent innovations in this field are mentioned.

An alternative method of extinguishing a small fire is by the use of a fire blanket, and this piece of equipment is briefly described at the end of the Part.

Chapter 2
Standards and specifications

1 British Standards

All types of portable extinguishers in common use are now covered by *BS 5423: Specification for portable fire extinguishers*, which sets out the recommended standards of construction, performance, marking and production testing. Most new extinguishers meet the specification, although there is no legal obligation for them to do so.

The bodies of high-pressure extinguishers (i.e. those with a working pressure of more than 25 bar) must comply with the requirements of *BS 5045: Transportable gas containers*.

Also relevant is *BS 5306 Part 3: Code of Practice for selection, installation and maintenance of portable fire extinguishers*. Reference to this should be made when consideration is being given to the siting, inspection and testing of extinguishers used by commercial and private undertakings.

For insurance purposes, the Fire Insurance Research and Technical Organisation (FIRTO) tests and approves extinguishers on behalf of the Loss Prevention Council, using separate criteria from those of the British Standards.

2 Certification

The certification of portable fire extinguishers, and of companies who manufacture, install or maintain them, is controlled by the British Approvals for Fire Equipment (BAFE). This organisation checks the production and quality control procedures of firms

Fig. 2.1 Certification markings. Left: BAFE symbol with Kitemark. Centre: BAFE symbol with Registered Firm mark. Right: BAFE logo.

against the appropriate part of BS 5750 (quality assessment schedules). BS 5423 and BS 5306 are approved Standards under this scheme. If all the requirements are met, the product or company concerned is authorised to display the BAFE symbol, incorporating the British Standards Institution kitemark (Fig. 2.1, left) or the Registered Firm symbol (centre) as the case may be. This may, if desired, be supplemented by the BAFE logo (right).

3 Types of extinguisher

Portable fire extinguishers can be divided into five categories according to the extinguishing medium they contain, namely:

(i)   Water   (iv) Halon
(ii) Foam   (v)   Carbon dioxide
(iii) Powder

Extinguishers are normally operated by the use of gas pressure in the upper part of the container which forces the extinguishing medium out through a nozzle. The required pressure is produced by one of the following methods:

(a) *Chemical reaction.* Two (or more) chemicals are allowed to react to produce an expellent gas when the operating mechanism is actuated. (This type of extinguisher is, for the most part, no longer used by brigades.)

(b) *Gas cartridge.* The pressure is produced by means of compressed or (more commonly) liquefied gas released from a gas cartridge fitted into the extinguisher.

(c) *Stored pressure.* The expellent gas is stored with the extinguishing medium in the body of the extinguisher which is thus permanently pressurised. In the case of carbon dioxide extinguishers, the expellent gas is itself the extinguishing medium.

To summarise, portable fire extinguishers may be classified by 'contents' and by 'method of operation' as shown in Table 1. The ticks indicate which combinations of types may be found.

Table 1

		CONTENTS				
		Water	Foam	Powder	Halon	CO$_2$
METHOD	Chemical	✓	✓			
OF	Gas cartridge	✓	✓	✓		
OPERATION	Stored pressure	✓	✓	✓	✓	✓

Since the use of chemical-type extinguishers is rapidly diminishing, it is considered unnecessary to deal with them in detail in this Book.

4 Performance requirements

The main requirements of BS 5423 regarding the performance of extinguishers are set out below.

a. Duration of discharge

The minimum duration of discharge specified for each type of extinguisher is shown in Table 2.

Table 2

		Minimum duration of discharge (secs)		
		Water	Foam	Others
Nominal charge of extinguisher (kg or litres)	Up to and including 2	10	10	6
	More than 2 but no more than 6	30	20	9
	More than 6 but no more than 10	45	30	12
	More than 10	45	30	15

b. Range of discharge

Water and foam extinguishers should be capable of maintaining a jet or spray of not less than:

4 m if the nominal charge is more than 2 litres; or
2 m if the nominal charge is not more than 2 litres,
for the minimum duration given in Table 2.

c. Proportion of contents discharged

The design of an extinguisher should be such that, when fully charged and operated in its normal working position, the proportion of the contents discharged is not less than:

(i)   water and foam: 95%

(ii)   powder (after full continuous discharge):   85%

(iii)   halon (during liquid phase of discharge):   85%

(iv) CO_2 (during liquid phase of discharge):   75%

d. Delay on operation

Not more than 4 seconds should elapse between the operation of the control mechanism and the commencement of discharge.

e. Rating of extinguishers

Extinguishers are given a rating denoting their extinguishing performance on class A and/or class B fires, according to the results of fire tests prescribed in BS 5423.

(1) Class A fires

For those extinguishers recommended for use on Class A fires (fires involving solid materials normally of an organic nature), the Standard provides for a series of wooden crib test fires. The cribs are of a standard height and width, but have varying lengths. An extinguisher is given a Class A rating corresponding to the largest standard wooden crib test fire that it can extinguish, e.g. a rating of 27A means that it is capable of extinguishing a standard Class A test fire 2.7 m in length.

(2) Class B fires

For Class B fires (fires involving liquids or liquefiable solids), the British Standard rating denotes the largest flammable liquid tray fire that can be extinguished by the extinguisher concerned, adopting the procedures specified. The liquid fuel used is one of a range of aliphatic hydrocarbons, to which a certain amount of water is added. The rating corresponds to the volume of liquid contained in the tray e.g. an extinguisher given a 34B rating is capable of extinguishing a fire in a tray containing 34 litres of fuel and water combined.

(3) Other fires

There is, at present, no performance rating for Class C fires (fires involving gases) or Class D fires (fires involving metals). Firemen, however, may occasionally use extinguishers for these purposes. Powder, halon and carbon dioxide extinguishers are suitable for gaseous fires, but great caution is necessary, and the gas supply should always be cut off first. There will otherwise be a risk of explosion once the fire has been extinguished. Chapter 5 Section 2b refers to powders suitable for metal fires.

NOTE: Water and foam extinguishers are generally considered unsuitable for dealing with fires in electrical equipment, due to the conductivity of these media.

f. Typical performances

Typical performance data for extinguishers of various types and sizes are given in Table 3.

Table 3

Characteristics of extinguishers

Type of extinguisher	Typical capacities	Charged weight	Range of discharge	Duration of discharge	Typical fire rating	
			(typical values)		A	B
Water	litres	kg	m	s		
	6	9–11	6	45	8	—
	9	12–15	6	70	13	—
Foam	6	10–11	4	27	8	144
	9	14–16	4	45	13	183
Powder	kg					
	1	1.5–2	3	8	5	34
	2	3–4	4	10	13	55
	3	5–6	4	10	13	113
	4	7.5–8.5	5	10	21	144
	6	9–11	5	12	34	183
	9	14–16	6	15	43	233
	12	18–20	6	20	55	296
Halon (1211)	1	1.5–3	2	8	—	21
	2.5	3–5	3	10	5	55
	3.5	5–7.5	5	11	5	89
	7	10–12	6	13	8	144
Carbon Dioxide	1	3–6	2	9	—	21
	2	4.5–8	2	14	—	34
	5	11–18	2	24	—	55
	7	17–23	3	26	—	55

5 Other requirements

The other main requirements of BS 5423 are set out in the following paragraphs.

a. Weight

The total weight of a fully-charged extinguisher should not exceed 23 kg. This is considered to be the maximum weight that a person can carry satisfactorily and use effectively.

b. Operating mechanism

Extinguishers should operate by piercing, opening and/or breaking a sealing device, without the need for inversion as in some older types. It should be apparent whether or not the extinguisher has been operated.

Extinguishers should include a device to prevent inadvertent operation, and a controllable discharge facility to enable the discharge to be interrupted.

c. Hose and nozzles

Extinguishers with a nominal charge of more than 3 kg or 3 litres should be fitted with a discharge hose and nozzle, the length of which should be not less than 80% of that of the extinguisher body. The hose should not be under pressure until the extinguisher is operated.

d. Marking of extinguishers

Extinguishers should be clearly marked with various specified items of information, including the following:

(i)   the words 'Fire extinguisher';

(ii)   the extinguishing medium;

(iii)   the type ('gas cartridge' or 'stored pressure');

(iv)   the nominal charge of the extinguishing medium in kg or litres;

(v)   the class of fire ('A' and/or 'B') for which the extinguisher is suitable, and the test rating(s) achieved (see Section 3e above);

(vi)   the method of operation and, on small water and foam extinguishers, the range of discharge;

(vii)   the BS number, i.e. BS 5423;

(viii) the temperature range over which the extinguisher will operate satisfactorily;

(ix)   the year of manufacture;

(x)   the test pressure and working pressure;

(xi)   whether the extinguisher is to be recharged or discarded after use.

In addition, high-pressure extinguishers should be marked to comply with the requirements of *BS 5045: Transportable gas containers*.

Gas cartridges also should be appropriately marked.

e. Colour of extinguishers

It is recommended that extinguishers be wholly or partly coloured as follows, for easy recognition:

Extinguishing medium	*Colour*
Water	Signal red
Foam	Pale cream
Powder	French blue
Carbon dioxide	Black
Halon	Emerald green

Most extinguishers at present comply with this recommendation (Fig. 2.2).

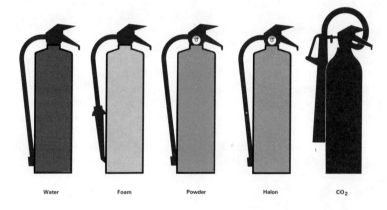

Water   Foam   Powder   Halon   CO₂

Fig. 2.2 The 5 basic types of extinguisher, showing the recommended colours. These colours may cover the entire body as shown, or only part of it, in which case the rest of the body may be either red or of self-coloured metal.

6 Periodic inspection and testing

a. Extinguishers on private or commercial premises

(1) Routine inspection by user

BS 5306 recommends that regular inspection of all extinguishers should be carried out by the user or his representative at intervals, to make sure that they are correctly positioned and charged and have suffered no obvious damage. The frequency of inspection should be not less than quarterly, and preferably at least monthly.

Extinguishers operated by means of a gas cartridge can be opened up for inspection, and the cartridge is checked by weighing to see if there is any loss of weight. In the case of powder (gas cartridge) extinguishers, the whole extinguisher is also weighed as an additional check. Stored pressure extinguishers cannot be opened up when charged; CO_2 extinguishers are checked by weighing, and other stored pressure extinguishers, according to type, are checked as follows:

(i)   the pressure is checked by a built-in pressure gauge or an independent manometer;

(ii)   the extinguisher is then weighed to check the amount of extinguishing medium.

(2) Annual inspection, service and maintenance

The user should arrange for extinguishers to be inspected and maintained by a suitably qualified person at least once a year. The person carrying out the inspection should identify and mark any extinguishers which are dangerous or otherwise defective. The user should be advised of any faulty or incorrectly installed extinguishers, and should take appropriate action. It is recommended that any soda-acid extinguishers (see Chapter 3), chemical foam extinguishers (see Chapter 4), or extinguishers containing halons other than Halon 1211 and Halon 1301 (see Chapter 6) should be removed from service. The dates of inspection should be recorded.

Recommended maintenance routines for the various types of extinguisher are given in BS 5306.

(3) Test discharge

It is recommended that all extinguishers be given a test discharge at intervals of between 4 and 20 years depending on their type. This may provide a convenient opportunity for the training of personnel in the use of extinguishers.

(4) Pressure testing

Halon and CO_2 extinguishers should undergo periodic pressure testing in accordance with BS 5430. These tests should be carried out by the manufacturer or some other specialist firm.

b. Fire brigade extinguishers

All extinguishers used and carried by fire brigades are required to be inspected and tested at regular intervals. Details of these tests and their frequencies are given in the *Fire Service Drill Book*, and reference should be made to them.

It should be noted that the intervals for tests of fire brigade extinguishers are shorter than those recommended in BS 5306 for extinguishers in commercial and private establishments.

7 Recharging of extinguishers

Extinguishers (other than the disposable types) should be recharged as soon as possible after use. Some types will need to be sent to manufacturers or other specialists, but others may be recharged by the user. In the latter case, the extinguisher should first be completely emptied and the old extinguishing medium discarded. The manufacturer's detailed instructions for recharging the particular type of extinguisher should be followed, and the extinguisher should be marked with the date of recharging.

Chapter 3
Water-type extinguishers

1 Soda-acid extinguisher

This type of extinguisher will still be found occasionally but it is rapidly being replaced by the water (gas cartridge) or water (stored pressure) types. The main drawback in the soda-acid extinguisher is that the chemical in the water ejected can damage surrounding material. It is not proposed to describe it in this Manual.

2 Water (gas cartridge) extinguisher

The water content of this plastic-lined steel cylinder is generally 9 or 6 litres and the expellent gas, usually CO_2, is contained in a cartridge fitted inside the body of the extinguisher.

The expelled liquid is pure water, although non-corrosive anti-freeze compounds can be added. The operating pressure is in the region of 10 bar. Fig. 3.1 shows a typical example of this type of extinguisher where removal of a safety pin or plug and pressure on the operating lever causes a pressure disc on the cartridge to be pierced, and at the same time opens a control valve. The release of gas exerts pressure on the surface of the water, forcing it up the discharge tube and out through the hose and nozzle. The discharge can be controlled by the operating lever.
Some extinguishers are operated by a striker instead of a lever. In these the discharge cannot be interrupted, and they therefore do not comply with BS 5423—See Chapter 2 Section 5b.

3 Water (stored pressure) extinguisher

This is of similar construction to the gas-cartridge type and of similar capacities, the difference being that the whole container is pressurised (Fig. 3.2). Air or nitrogen is pumped into it through a special adaptor in the operating head until the pressure reaches about 10 bar.

The extinguisher is operated by removing the safety pin or plug and squeezing the operating lever. This opens the control valve and allows the pressurised air to expel the water. Again, the discharge can be controlled by the lever.

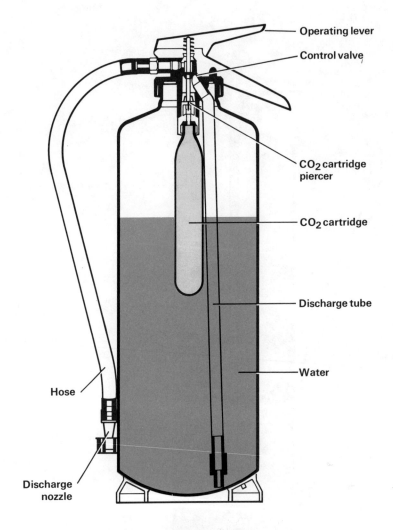

Fig. 3.1 Water extinguisher (gas-cartridge type).

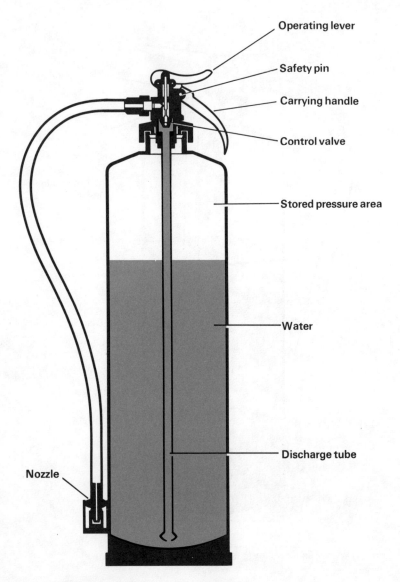

Fig. 3.2 Water extinguisher (stored-pressure type).

Chapter 4
Foam extinguishers

1 General

Although protein foam concentrate is still often used in the large foam-making branch application, portable foam extinguishers now mainly use aqueous film-forming foam (AFFF) concentrate. Details of the different types of foam concentrate and the properties of foam will be found in Part 3.

There are basically two ways of producing foam from portable extinguishers:

(i) by chemical reaction;

(ii) by self-aspiration of a foam solution through a foam branchpipe.

There is also the method of applying AFFF as a non-aspirated spray.

A recent development is a fluoroprotein film-forming foam (FFFP) extinguisher which can tackle Class A and B fires, including those involving 'polar' products (alcohols etc.) on which most foam extinguishers are ineffective. This is usually applied as an aspirated foam.

2 Chemical foam extinguishers

These have now largely been replaced by more modern types. The chemical reaction in the extinguisher produces a foam containing CO_2 bubbles, and the gas pressure itself causes the discharge.

3 Self-aspirating foam extinguishers

Here a foam solution (foam concentrate in water) is stored in a container, usually of 6 or 9 litre capacity, and either discharged by a gas-cartridge of CO_2 fitted in the body of the extinguisher (Fig. 4.1) or by compressed air or nitrogen which has been pumped into the container by the method described in Chapter 3 (Fig. 4.2). In both cases the solution is forced out through the delivery hose and aspirated by the specially designed branch, which is of the low-expansion type as described in Part 3. The operating pressure is usually about 10 bar, and all types can be used with some kind of low-freeze depressant, but the manufacturer's instructions for this must be carefully followed.

Operation is either by striker (Fig. 4.1) or lever to pierce the gas-cartridge pressure disc or, in the stored-pressure type, a lever to open a valve (Fig. 4.2). Extinguishers operated by a striker do not have a controllable discharge, and therefore do not comply with BS 5423.

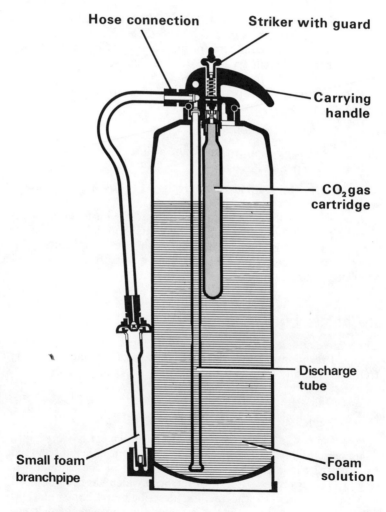

Fig. 4.1 Foam extinguisher (gas-cartridge type).

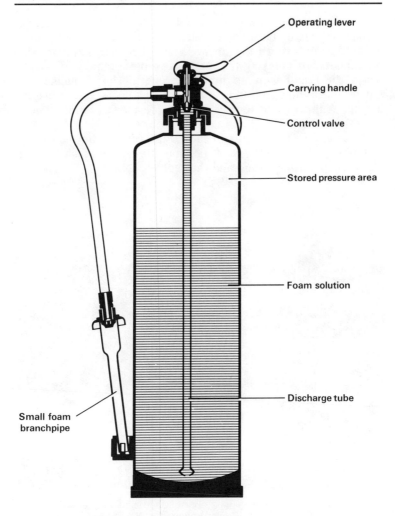

Operating lever

Carrying handle

Control valve

Stored pressure area

Foam solution

Discharge tube

Small foam branchpipe

Fig. 4.2 Foam extinguisher (stored-pressure type).

4 Non-aspirating AFFF extinguisher

This is usually a gas-cartridge-operated type with a modified nozzle which sprays the AFFF onto the fire.

5 Use of foam extinguishers

When using a self-aspirating foam extinguisher on a contained fire, the operator should, if possible, direct the foam against a vertical surface e.g. a wall or side of the container (Fig. 4.3). This allows the foam to run down and form a spreading blanket on the surface of the burning material. Any discharge directly onto a liquid could disturb the surface and either mix the foam with the liquid, thus breaking the foam down more rapidly, or sink it below the liquid with no inhibiting effect. This is unlikely to happen with non-aspirating spray-type extinguishers, however, and the foam from these may therefore be allowed to fall directly onto the surface of the liquid.

On a running fire, the foam should fall gently onto the surface to build up the blanket and, if possible, to make a break between the already burning liquid and that not yet ignited.

Fig. 4.3 The discharge from a foam extinguisher should be directed so that the foam builds up a blanket which will flow over the burning liquid.

Chapter 5
Powder extinguishers

1 General

Powders used to extinguish or control fires are composed essentially of very small particles of an appropriate chemical or chemicals. These are treated with flow additives to give resistance to moisture absorption and caking during storage and to give a free flow when discharged through hoses and nozzles. Different chemicals are effective on different Classes of fire, which are defined on page 18 and can be briefly categorised as follows:

Class A—solids (wood, paper, textiles etc.);
Class B—flammable liquids;
Class C—gases;
Class D—metals.

Powders are classified according to their potential application e.g. BC, ABC.

2 Types of powder

a. Class BC powders

These powders extinguish fire mainly by means of a chemical reaction which inhibits flame propagation.

The most effective powders for use against Class BC fires are based on the salts of the alkali metals. The chlorides and sulphates are effective, but relatively corrosive. In general, the most useful powders for Class BC fires have been found to be based on the bicarbonates of sodium and potassium, a particularly effective one being a complex combination of urea and potassium bicarbonate (Monnex).

b. Class ABC ('general purpose') powders

These powders not only inhibit flame, like the BC type, but also suppress the smouldering type of combustion found in Class A fires. When applied to solid material, they form a crust over it by the action of heat on the powder. Oxygen is excluded and a smothering effect obtained. This crust must be left undisturbed for the material to cool below its ignition temperature.

The most popular Class ABC powder is based on mono ammonium phosphate.

c. Class D powders

In the UK, neither of the above types of powder are considered adequate for dealing with Class D fires e.g. those involving magnesium, aluminium, or titanium. Special powders have been developed which are capable of extinguishing, or at least controlling, this type of fire.

One type of such powder is a combination of sodium, potassium and barium chlorides known as ternary eutectic chloride (TEC), which has proved effective against fires in uranium, plutonium and magnesium alloy. It forms a smothering crust over the metal, while also helping to cool it. The melting point of the powder is comparatively low and its capacity for absorbing latent heat from the metal relatively high.

3 Operational considerations

a. Hazards to personnel

Firemen must bear in mind that, although most powders are of minimal toxicity, some, especially those employing chlorides e.g. TEC, can be dangerous if inhaled for any length of time. No powder is pleasant to inhale or get in the eyes so, especially when discharging an extinguisher in a confined space, personnel should be careful and ventilate when conditions permit. When refilling extinguishers or handling powders, particularly those containing chloride, personnel should wear suitable masks.

b. Firefighting

Powder has a rate of application per unit of fire volume (or area) below which it will not extinguish the fire. This is known as the critical application rate.

Whilst powders can suppress a fire they do not normally form an inerting atmosphere and will rapidly settle out once application stops. Fireman must always beware of re-ignition, especially on Class B fires, and be ready to begin powder application again or to use another suitable medium. The efficacy of powder on an outdoor fire will depend on circumstances e.g. wind and moisture, and application rates may need to be increased by up to 50%.

Powder is a particularly useful medium for shallow fires requiring rapid extinction, e.g. running fuel fires. On the other hand, it is not good at penetrating hidden spaces, and it may cause damage if used on delicate machinery. It also tends to obscure visibility in confined spaces.

c. Mixing of powders

As each fire brigade usually uses only one type of powder, cross-contamination or chemical reaction of different powders is unlikely. However, firemen may find themselves using their own extinguishers to back up industrial or commercial fire teams using an incompatible powder.

If there is any reaction it will be very slow but some mixtures can, after some delay, react, forming water and CO_2 with a possible pressure build-up if in a closed container.

4 Types of powder extinguishers

Portable powder extinguishers are available in sizes ranging from 1 to 12 kg of powder content. The methods of expelling the powder from the container are similar to those of water and foam extinguishers, i.e. stored pressure or gas cartridge. Fig. 5.1 shows

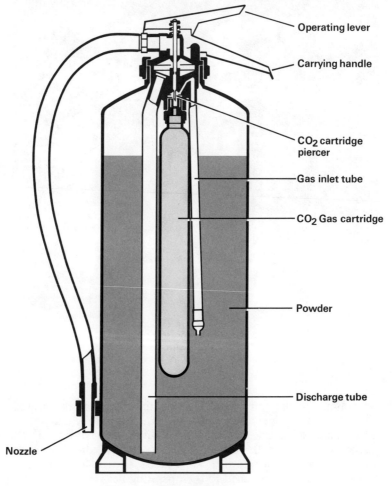

Fig. 5.1 Powder extinguisher (gas-cartridge type).

Fig. 5.2 Powder extinguishers (stored-pressure type). (1) with fan-shaped nozzle fitted to the operating head. (2) with fan-shaped nozzle at the end of a short length of hose. (3) Air valve adaptor in position for re-charging.

an example of the latter type. The pressurised gas, when released, 'fluidifies' the powder and ejects it via a discharge tube and nozzle. The design of nozzle varies, some extinguishers having a fan-shaped type (Fig. 5.2). Also in the larger models, the nozzle is at the end of a short length of hose, whereas the smaller types have the nozzle directly attached to the operating head.

Operating pressures vary from about 7.5 to 15 bar.

a. Stored pressure type

This type is pressurised in the same way as the corresponding type of water or foam extinguisher, i.e. air or nitrogen is pumped in until the fitted gauge (see Fig. 5.2) registers the required pressure. Operation requires the safety pin or plug to be removed and the lever squeezed. The flow of powder can be controlled by the lever.

b. Gas-cartridge type

Extinguishers of this type have a suitable size of CO_2 gas cartridge fitted inside the container. Following removal of the safety pin or plug, either (a) the knob on top is struck or (b) the lever is squeezed. In the case of (a) there is a squeeze-grip discharge control on the end of the delivery hose. On some models the CO_2, when released from the cartridge, flows to the bottom of the container via a gas inlet tube (Fig. 5.1). This helps the powder to fluidify.

5 Exclusion of moisture when recharging

It is essential, in the case of powder extinguishers, that both the extinguisher itself and any air pumped into it should be free of moisture, and that the new powder charge should be kept completely dry. If an air line is used, an efficient water trap must be provided to prevent any condensed moisture being inadvertently admitted to the extinguisher. When refilling, once the new powder container is opened, the powder should be transferred immediately into the extinguisher, which should then be sealed.

Chapter 6
Halon extinguishers

1 General

Halons (a contraction of 'halogenated hydrocarbons') are a group of extinguishing agents which are stored under pressure in liquid form and released in such a way as to vaporise rapidly in a fire zone. They extinguish fire mainly by interfering with the chemical reactions involved in the propagation of flame, and they possess little cooling effect. This chapter considers the general properties of halons, before looking at their use in portable extinguishers. Their other main application—in fixed installations—is dealt with in the *Manual*, Book 9 Chapter 8 Section 5.

Halons find their main application in their rapid knockdown effect on small or incipient Class B or C fires, especially in confined spaces. They may also be used in preference to foam on fires involving rapidly flowing liquids, where quick extinction is the prime consideration. In Class A fires, they may be used but are much less efficient. They are electrically non-conductive, so are particularly safe to use on electrical or electronic equipment and cause little damage.

NB Halon 1301 (see Section 3), due to its very low boiling point, will emerge as a gas but other halons, with higher boiling points, emerge as liquids, which gives them a better throw.

2 Characteristics

Halons are hydrocarbon compounds of a group of 5 non-metallic elements known as halogens, i.e. fluorine, chlorine, bromine, iodine and astatine. For various reasons iodine and astatine are not suitable as extinguishants and can be ignored. The physical properties of the best known halons are given in Table 4, plus CO_2 for comparison.

The criteria determining the suitability of halons for firefighting are:

(i)   Their efficiency as extinguishing agents;

(ii) their toxicity, including that of their products on decomposition;

(iii)   their physical properties e.g. boiling and freezing points;

(iv)   their effect on materials with which they come in contact.

3 Identification

In order to simplify the rather involved chemical formulae of the halons, a numbering system has been devised. As shown in Table 4 the number of atoms of carbon, fluorine, chlorine and bromine in each halon molecule are counted, terminal zeros are ignored and the resultant 3 or 4 figure number is used. The actual names of the halons are already shortened to sets of initial letters as under.

Name	Initials	Halon No.
Bromotrifluoromethane	BTM	1301
Bromochlorodifluoromethane	BCF	1211
Dibromotetrafluoroethane	DTE	2402
Chlorobromomethane	CBM	1011
Carbon tetrachloride	CTC	104
Methyl bromide	MB	1001

4 Toxicity

The relative toxicities of halons were formerly assessed by the ratio between the 'extinguishing concentration' and the 'dangerous concentration'; this was known as the 'R' factor (see Table 4). A Technical Sub-Committee of the CFBAC concluded that any halon whose 'R' factor exceeded 4 was not suitable in portable fire extinguishers used by brigades. A further appraisal by the Fire Research Station in 1977 (Fire Research Note Number 1073) used a more meaningful assessment of halons based on their actual effect on man (previously tests had been on animals). Here the extinguishing concentration was divided by the concentration which will give rise to early symptoms of narcosis; this ratio is known as the 'F' factor, which is also shown in Table 4. The table shows that Halons 1301 and 1211 are the least toxic; the exposure of personnel to these agents during the course of fire-fighting is likely to be well within the maximum safe values shown (column 10), except where a total flooding system is being discharged.

In a fire situation, a further aspect to be considered is the effect of the decomposition products of halons, which are generally much more toxic than the halons themselves. However, it is the combustion products of the actual fire, e.g. smoke, carbon monoxide, that present the greatest hazard. The normal safety precautions against these (i.e. BA where appropriate, and sub-

Table 4

Physical properties of halons and carbon dioxide

1 Agent	2 Chemical symbols	3 Atoms in the molecule				4 Boiling point at 1 atm °C	5 Freezing point °C	6 Inhibitory factor (V/V n-Heptane)	7 'F' factor	8 'R' factor	9 Toxicity rating[a]	10 Maximum safe exposure to agent for Man
		C	F	Cl	Br							
BTM	$CBrF_3$	1	3	0	1	−57.6	−168	3.5%	0.8	0.1	6	7–10% for 1 min
BCF	$CBrClF_2$	1	2	1	1	−4	−160.5	3.8%	4.5	0.2	5	4–5% for 1 min
DTE	$C_2Br_2F_4$	2	4	0	2	47.5	−110.5	2.1%	14.0	0.4	4	—
CBM	CH_2BrCl	1	0	1	1	67.8	−86	4.5%	64	2.4	3	—
CTC	CCl_4	1	0	4	0	76.7	−22.8		129	8.1	3	—
MB	CH_3Br	1	0	0	1	4.5	−93.7	5.1%	11.8	2		—
Carbon dioxide	CO_2					−78.5[b]		20.5%	6	2.8	5	9% for 10 mins

[a] Highest figure is the least toxic.   [b] Sublimation point (see page 42).

sequent ventilation) should be sufficient to eliminate any dangers arising from the decomposition of those halons that are currently used. Where the size of the fire does not warrant the use of BA, firemen may experience some irritation of the eyes, throat etc., but this will be only temporary.

Halon 1301, because of its low boiling point ($-57.6°C$), can cause 'low temperature burns' if the liquid comes into contact with the skin.

5 Fire extinction efficiency

The fire extinction efficiency of a halon can be measured precisely by the effect of the compound on the flammable limits of combustion vapours such as hexane or heptane. The figure obtained is known as the 'inhibitory factor', and the lower the inhibitory factor of a halon the better its extinction efficiency. It can be seen from column 6 in Table 4 that Halon 2402 is the most efficient and Halon 1301 second.

Firemen should, however, remember that, because a halon has very little cooling effect on a fire (even less than that of CO_2), re-ignition can easily occur following its discharge from a portable extinguisher. Back-up supplies of halons or other suitable extinguishing media should therefore be available.

6 Use of particular halons

Because of the various strictures above, the 3 halons found in general use are 1301, 1211 and, to a lesser extent, 1011. However, 2402 is making an appearance in some aircraft engine systems in Italy and for ship firefighting in the USSR. It was included in a list of suitable extinguishing agents on the basis of information contained in Fire Research Note Number 860 but has not found much support in the UK.

At the present time, the great majority of portable halon extinguishers in this country use Halon 1211.

7 Non-use of halons

Halons should not be used on:

(a) chemicals containing their own oxygen e.g. cellulose nitrate, gunpowder and solid rocket propellants;

(b) reactive metals e.g. sodium, potassium, magnesium, titanium;

(c) metal hydrides e.g. lithium aluminium hydride and sodium hydride.

8 Types of extinguishers

Portable halon extinguishers commonly range from 0.7 kg to 7 kg and are invariably of the stored-pressure type. They are normally pressurised to about 10 bar with dry nitrogen, to ensure efficient discharge. Most halon extinguishers have their discharge controlled by a lever (see Fig. 6.1 and Fig. 6.2) but a few designs have a striker, which may or may not give a controllable discharge.

Several manufacturers incorporate some sort of pressure indicator and/or a method of showing whether the extinguisher has been used; the latter is now a requirement of BS 5423. By their design, halon extinguishers, once used, need to be recharged either in workshops or by the manufacturers or other specialists. Some smaller types feature an expendable body, the operating mechanism being capable of removal and replacement on another cartridge. Some others are completely disposable.

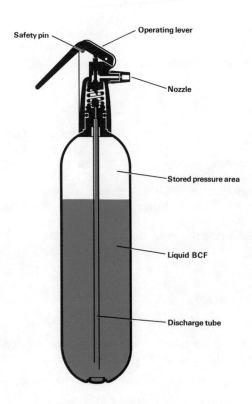

Fig. 6.1 Halon extinguisher (small size).

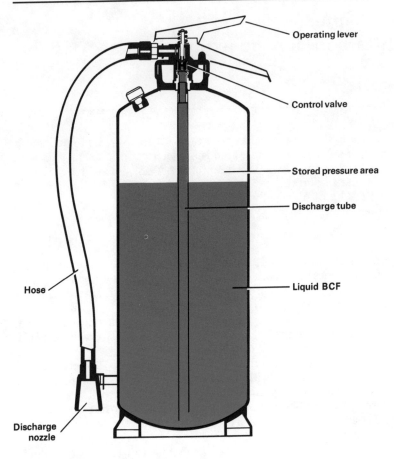

Fig. 6.2 Halon extinguisher (large size).

Chapter 7
Carbon dioxide extinguishers

Carbon dioxide (CO_2) has been used for many years to extinguish fires involving flammable liquids or electrical equipment. It is used in fixed installations (see the *Manual*, Book 9 Chapter 8 Section 4), and in portable extinguishers with capacities ranging from 0.9 to 6.8 kg of liquefied gas.

1 General characteristics of CO_2

CO_2 has a number of properties making it useful for extinguishing fire. It does not react with most substances, it provides its own pressure for discharge from an extinguisher and, since it emerges as a gas, it can penetrate to all parts of a fire area. It is a non-conductor of electricity and will not damage electronic equipment. Its uses are generally similar to those of halons, except that it is not recommended for Class A fires.

The physical properties of CO_2 are shown in Table 4 on page 38 in comparison with halons. It is relatively non-toxic, and, unlike halons, does not decompose in a fire, so it produces no toxic by-products. A dangerous level of exposure to CO_2 (see Table 4) is very unlikely to result from the use of portable extinguishers.

When liquid CO_2 is released from a pressurised storage cylinder there is an extremely rapid expansion from liquid to gas which produces a refrigerating effect that converts part of the CO_2 into 'snow' (i.e. solid particles). This snow, which has a temperature of about $-79°C$, soon sublimes (i.e. changes directly from solid to gas). This sublimation produces some cooling effect, but it is the smothering effect of the gas which is of primary importance in the extinguishing process. In general, 1 kg of liquid CO_2 will produce about 0.5 m^3 of free gas at atmospheric pressure.

2 Portable CO_2 extinguishers

CO_2 extinguishers (Figs. 7.1 and 7.2) consist basically of a pressure cylinder, a control valve for releasing the gas, and a discharge horn for applying the gas onto the fire. On the smaller models the discharge horn is connected directly to the operating head, whereas the larger sizes have a short pipe or flexible high-pressure

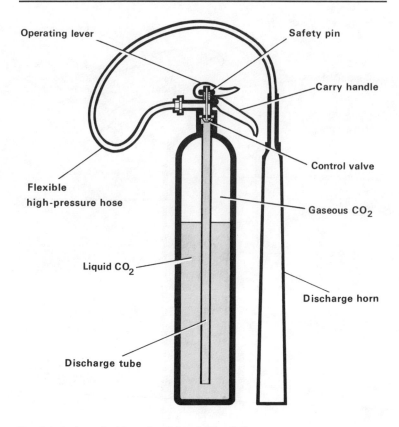

Fig. 7.1 Carbon dioxide extinguisher (large size).

hose and the discharge horn is connected to the end of the pipe or hose. The extinguisher must incorporate a relief device to prevent excessive pressure build-up; this can be seen in Fig. 7.2.

The CO_2 is retained in a liquid condition in the cylinder under about 56 bar pressure at normal temperature of 20°C. The cylinder is usually filled with liquid CO_2 to approximately two-thirds of its total capacity. A small amount of CO_2 evaporates and fills the top third of the cylinder, and it is this gas which acts as the expellant.

Some earlier models were operated by striking a plunger at the head of the cylinder and this pierced a sealing disc, but in most current models the gas is released by first removing a safety pin and then operating the discharge lever.

Owing to the expansion of the discharging gas and its liability to freeze, careful design of the discharge mechanism is essential. A discharge tube is fitted into the cylinder so that liquid CO_2

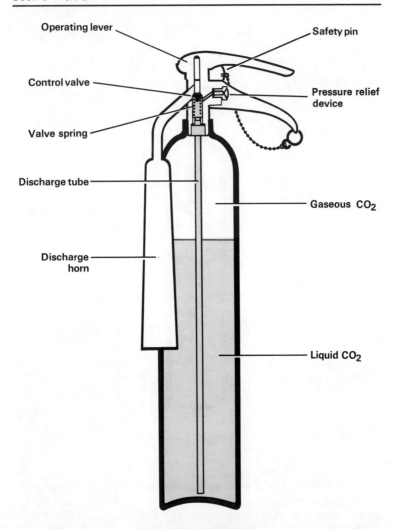

Fig. 7.2 Carbon dioxide extinguisher (small size).

from the bottom of the cylinder is released through the valve in the cylinder head. This valve should open quickly and provide a clear passage for the CO_2. Expansion may commence in the flexible hose, if fitted, but it mostly takes place in the discharge horn, which is used to direct the gas onto the seat of the fire. The ratio of expansion is approximately 450:1. The design of the discharge horn is a very important feature; its main purpose is to stop the entrainment of air with the CO_2 by reducing the velocity of the gas. Without this horn, the jet of CO_2 gas and air would act like a blow-torch and increase the intensity of the fire.

3 Use of CO_2 extinguishers

CO_2 extinguishers are carried on some fire brigade appliances, but will more often be found as part of the firefighting equipment in commercial or industrial premises. Portable CO_2 extinguishers are often installed in kitchens in hotels and large restaurants, and in fish frying establishments, since CO_2 does not contaminate the frying oil when discharged onto it. The same precautions should be taken when handling them as with any other compressed gas cylinder.

The discharge horn should be directed at the heart of the fire, starting at one edge and sweeping across the surface of the burning material (Fig. 7.3). It should be noted that the discharge range of a CO_2 extinguisher is fairly limited (see Table 3). If it is necessary to use such an extinguisher in the open air, the operator should stand up-wind of the fire and apply the gas in a down-wind direction, as close as possible to the fire.

Fig. 7.3 Method of operating a CO_2 extinguisher by sweeping the discharge horn across the surface of the burning material.

After a CO_2 extinguisher has been used indoors and the fire extinguished, the room should be adequately ventilated. Owing to the intense cold generated on discharge, the gas should not be directed onto exposed parts of the body, nor should the cylinder, hose or discharge horn be held with the bare hands except where a handgrip is provided on the horn.

Other points which may be mentioned are:

(i)   The gas makes a considerable noise during discharge and, if the fireman has not used such an extinguisher before, the sound may take him off his guard and cause him to misdirect the jet for the first vital seconds.

(ii) CO_2 issues from the extinguisher in the form of a very dense vapour which, in a confined space, will impair visibility considerably.

(iii) Since CO_2 has no substantial cooling effect on the burning materials, it is essential that a CO_2 extinguisher should always be backed up with additional CO_2 extinguishers or other media, in case re-ignition should occur.

(iv) CO_2 extinguishers should be sent to the manufacturers or other specialist firms for recharging.

Chapter 8
Fire blankets

A method of tackling small fires, e.g. in chip pans, is by smothering with a fire blanket. This is usually available packed into a small container designed to give a quick release to the blanket.

BS 6575: Specification for fire blankets specifies two types of blanket:

(a) *light duty* for extinguishing small fires in containers of cooking fats or oils, or fires in clothing worn by people;

(b) *heavy duty* for industrial applications, to resist penetration by molten metal e.g. in cutting or welding operations, and to protect against radiant heat, in addition to the uses mentioned in (a) above.

The BS also specifies that blankets generally shall have no edge longer than 1.8 m, light duty types no edge shorter than 0.9 m

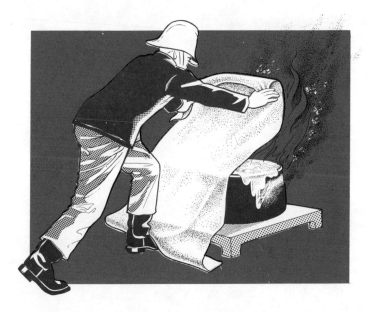

Fig. 8.1 Smothering a small fire with a fire blanket. Note how the fireman holds the blanket to protect his face and body from the heat.

and heavy duty no edge shorter than 1.2 m. The mass must be no more than 10 kg.

Some brigades carry a fire blanket on an appliance, and it is useful in protecting trapped people when the brigade have to resort to hot-cutting to extricate them. The action of using a fire blanket to extinguish a fire is illustrated in Fig. 8.1.

The materials used for fire blankets vary, but most of those currently in use are either of fibreglass or leather.

Part 3
Foam and foam-making equipment

Introduction

Fires in flammable liquids are difficult and, in some cases, impossible to extinguish with water even in the form of spray or fog. Some of the most hazardous substances have a specific gravity lower than that of water and are not miscible with water, and their flashpoint is often not much higher than the temperature of the water applied. Flammable liquids give off vapour and, within the flammable limits of the substance, it is this vapour that burns. It is many years since firefighting foams were developed which were able to float on the liquid and create a barrier between the vapour and the air, and thus extinguish the flames. There is a complex relationship between the properties of foam, its performance under different fire conditions and the best method of applying it to a fire. Although much work has been done on the problems, development is still going on.

The sort of questions involved relate to:

(a) *Stability*: after application, the ability of the foam to retain its liquid content, i.e. the time it takes for the liquid to drain from the foam.

(b) *Expansion*: ability of the foam solution, where necessary, to foam when passed through aspirating nozzles.

(c) *Burn-back resistance* (*security*): the ability of a foam blanket to provide security against re-ignition.

(d) *Flow*: ability of the foam to be projected and to flow across the liquid to be extinguished and/or protected.

(e) *Contamination resistance*: ability of the foam to resist contamination by the flammable liquid leading to foam destruction.

It must be understood that different risks will require different combinations of foam characteristics and different means of applying the foam. These needs have been responsible for the parallel development of two kinds of foams:

(i)   Protein-based foams;

(ii) Synthetic foams;

and a variety of both aspirating and non-aspirating equipment to apply them to incidents. The following chapters describe the different types of foam and some of the equipment.

In order to prevent confusion, the reader's attention is drawn to the following definitions of terms used in this Part:

Application rate (*high expansion*)   The rate measured in cubic metres per square metre per minute ($m^3/m^2/min$) of foam.

Application rate (*low and medium expansion*)   The flow requirement per area measured in litres per square metre per minute ($l/m^2/min$) of foam solution.

Aspiration   The entrainment of air into the stream of foam solution.

Concentration   The percentage of foam concentrate mixed with the water.

Discharge rate (*high expansion*)   The discharge rate of a high expansion foam generator measured in cubic metres/min (m^3/min) of foam at a stated expansion ratio.

Drainage time   The time taken for a percentage of the liquid content of a foam sample of a stated depth to drain to the bottom. For low expansion foam, this is 25%; for medium and high expansion foams it is 50%.

Expansion ratio   The ratio of the volume of foam solution to the volume of finished foam.

Finished foam   The foam as applied to the fire. It may be *aspirated* (foam concentrate + water + air) or *non-aspirated* (foam concentrate + water only).

Flow requirement (*low and medium expansion*)   The nominal supply rate of foam solution required by a foam branchpipe, measured in litres/min.

Foam concentrate   The foam as supplied by the manufacturer in liquid form; this is sometimes referred to as 'compound', 'liquid' or by trade or brand names.

Foam generator (*high expansion*)   A mechanical device in which foam solution is sprayed onto a net screen through which air is being forced by a fan.

Foam generator (*low expansion*)   Similar to a FMB, but inserted in a line of hose so that the finished foam passes along the hose to a discharge nozzle.

Foam-making branch (*FMB*)   The equipment by which the foam solution is normally aspirated.

Foam monitor   A larger version of a FMB which cannot be hand-held.

Foam solution   A solution of foam concentrate in water at the appropriate concentration.

Induction   The entrainment of foam concentrate into the water stream.

Inline inductor   A device inserted in a hose line in order to induce the foam concentrate before the water reaches the FMB.

Polar fuels   Generally water-miscible solvents, e.g. alcohols, ketones. They require special alcohol-resistant foam concentrates.

Shear stress   The measurement of the stiffness of a foam sample. This is dependent on the size of the bubbles.

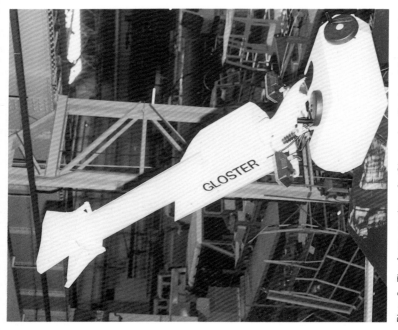

Plate 2. The foam monitor of a Gloster Javelin airport foam tender.

Photo: Gloster Saro Limited

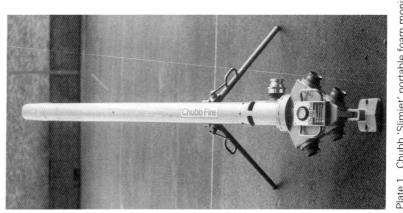

Plate 1. Chubb 'Slimjet' portable foam monitor.

Photo: County of Avon Fire Brigade

Plate 3. Angus Mini-Turbex high expansion foam generator.
Photo: Angus Fire Armour Limited

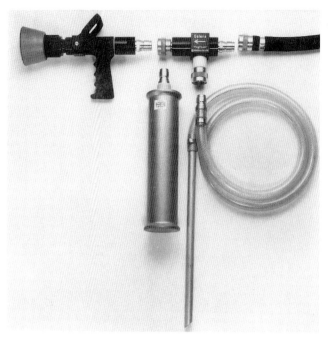

Plate 4. Galena 'Fog Foam' hose-reel foam unit.
Photo: Galena (Fire Engineering) Limited

Plate 5. An example of a distribution manifold for use with a pressurised foam concentrate supply.
Photo: County of Avon Fire Brigade

Plate 6. Part of a typical foam tender, showing various items of equipment including LX foam branchpipes, inline inductors, monitors and a Mobrey

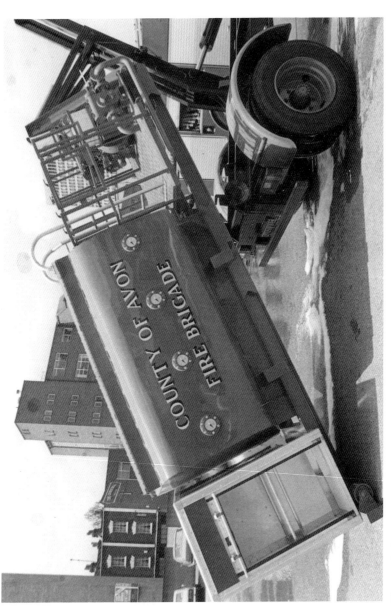

Plate 7. A demountable-pod foam system.
Photo: County of Avon Fire Brigade

Plate 8. Another version of a demountable-pod foam system, including a foam tank, foam branchpipe, monitor, and high expansion foam generator.

Photo: West Midlands Fire Service

Plate 9. Another view of the pod system shown in Plate 8.

Photo: West Midlands Fire Service

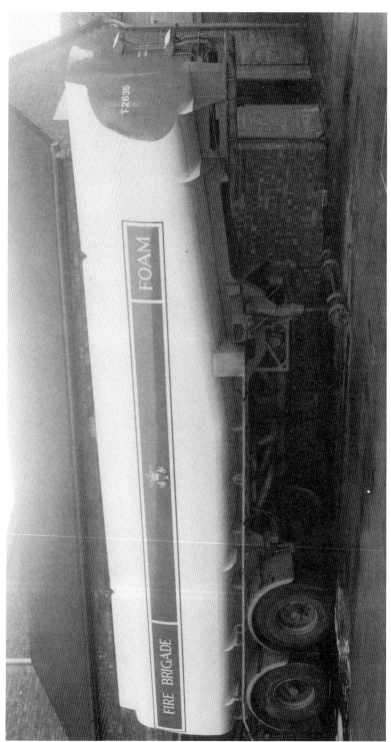

Plate 10. A foam tank trailer unit with a capacity of 28,000 litres of foam concentrate.

Photo: County of Avon Fire Brigade

Plate 11. The application of foam onto a crashed tanker train carrying gas oil.
Photo: *Greater Manchester County Fire Service*

Chapter 9
Types and properties of foam

1 Foam concentrates

a. General

Foam concentrates are a concentrated aqueous solution of carefully selected foaming agents and surfactants such as hydrolised proteins or fluoro-chemicals. Depending on the particular purpose for which they will be used, they will have various other additives.

In addition to their ability to produce foam for extinction of fires, other properties are also important e.g. temperature effect on induction rate, undesirable effects on personnel, pollution of water-courses.

To ensure that foam concentrates are suitable, they are tested against either Defence Standards or, in the case of high expansion foam (HX), against a JCAEU (JCDD) specification.

Foam concentrates are grouped according to their chemical constituents as follows.

b. Protein (P)

These are liquids containing hydrolised protein materials, with certain salts added to improve stability and storage. They are usually manufactured for use at 3% and 6% concentrations, and the foam produced

(i)   is very stable;

(ii) is relatively slow-flowing with a high shear stress;

(iii) has a very good burn-back resistance;

(iv) has poor contamination resistance.

c. Fluoroprotein (FP)

These are made from protein-based concentrates by the addition of fluorinated and other types of surface-active agents. They are usually available for use at 3% or 6% concentrations.

Fluoroprotein foam

(i)   flows more quickly across the fuel surface;

(ii) has good re-sealing properties;

(iii)   has very good burn-back resistance;

(iv)   is less likely to be contaminated by hydrocarbon fuels.

d. Synthetic (S)

These are based upon mixtures of water-soluble surface-active agents derived from hydrocarbons with additional stabilizers. They are used at 1% to 6% concentrations.

Synthetic foam:

(i)   flows more freely than P foam;

(ii)   has a tendency to mix with the fuel;

(iii) has poor burn-back resistance;

(iv)   has good storage properties.

e. Film-forming types

These concentrates produce a foam which, when used in suitable circumstances, has the ability to form a thin transparent film over the surface of the fuel, which helps to prevent re-ignition. There are two types of film-forming concentrate, as described below. Both can be used to make either aspirated or non-aspirated foam.

(1) Aqueous Film Forming Foam (AFFF) concentrate

This is based on fluorinated surface-active agents with other surface-active agents and stabilizers. The characteristics of AFFF are as follows:

(i)   it is more fluid than P, FP or S foam;

(ii)   it has quick control and extinction properties;

(iii) it has a fast drainage rate;

(iv)   the liquid draining out floats on the fuel surface, thereby forming the film;

(v)   its re-sealing capability is good;

(vi)   it has a reasonably good burn-back resistance;

(vii) its contamination resistance is moderate.

AFFF concentrates are usually designed for 1, 3 or 6% use.

(2) Film Forming Fluoroprotein (FFFP) concentrate

This consists of a combination of protein and fluorinated surface-active agents and stabilizers. The foam produced has similar characteristics to AFFF, but its burn-back resistance may be superior, and its resistance to fuel contamination is excellent.

FFFP is usually available for use at 3% and 6% concentrations.

f. Alcohol resistant (AR)

This consists of P, FP or FFFP foam concentrate with an added polymer ingredient which, by precipitation, forms a thin fuel-insoluble 'skin' or membrane at the interface between the fuel and the foam. The effectiveness of such foam depends on the water-miscible (polar) fuel involved and the method of application.

2 Production of foam

a. General

Foam is produced by mixing the foam concentrate with water in the correct proportions, and then, if appropriate, aspirating the resulting solution into a mass of bubbles. In this state it is often referred to as 'finished foam'. When foam is made, there are 3 factors which can be varied:

(i)   the proportion of foam concentrate added to the water, i.e. the concentration;

(ii)   the volume of air mixed with each volume of foam solution, i.e. the expansion;

(iii) in the case of MX and HX foams, the size of the bubbles.

These three factors will greatly influence the behaviour of the foam when it is applied to a fire.

b. Concentration

This is determined by the induction equipment selected. On some equipment, it can be varied by calibrated controls. The appropriate concentration, e.g. 3%, 6%, will vary according to the kind of concentrate used (see Section 1 above), and will be indicated by the manufacturer.

c. Expansion

This is determined by (a) the type of foam concentrate used, (b) the concentration, (c) the design of the FMB or generator and (d) the operating pressure. In some HX generators, such as the Angus Turbex II, the expansion can also be varied by adjustments to the controls.

Foams can be divided into three categories according to their expansion, as follows:

(1) Low expansion (LX)

Expansion ratio from 2:1 to 20:1, but usually between 5:1 and 15:1. Produced in aspirated form by FMBs or mechanical generators, or in non-aspirated form from standard water-delivering devices.

(2) Medium expansion (MX)

Expansion ratio from 20:1 to 200:1, but usually between 50:1 and 150:1. Produced by special FMBs with gauze meshes.

(3) High expansion (HX)

Expansion ratio from 200:1 to 2000:1, but usually no more than about 1200:1. Produced by generators with air fans and nets, using synthetic concentrate.

The expansion of foam is measured by comparing the weight of a known volume of the finished foam with that of an equal volume of the unaspirated foam solution, i.e.:

$$\frac{\text{weight of volume of foam solution}}{\text{weight of same volume of finished foam}} = \text{expansion} \quad \text{(Fig. 9.1(1))}$$

Chapter 11 gives details of the behaviour and suitability of foams according to their expansion category.

d. Bubble size

The size of the bubbles in MX and HX foam is determined by the size of the mesh or net in the foam-making equipment.

3. Quality of foam

a. General

Good foam quality depends on:

(i)   suitable type of concentrate used for the task in hand;

(ii)   concentrate in good condition;

(iii)   concentrate used at the correct concentration;

(iv)   good design of equipment;

(v)   good maintenance of equipment;

(vi)   correct pump pressure for the equipment in use.

Two important factors determining (i) above are the drainage time and shear stress of the resulting foam. These factors are explained below; their values for particular concentrates under specified conditions can be obtained from the manufacturers.

b. Drainage time

This is measured by taking the time for a selected percentage of the liquid content of the foam to drain out after foaming ceases (see Fig. 9.1(2)). LX foams are measured to 25% and MX and HX to 50%.

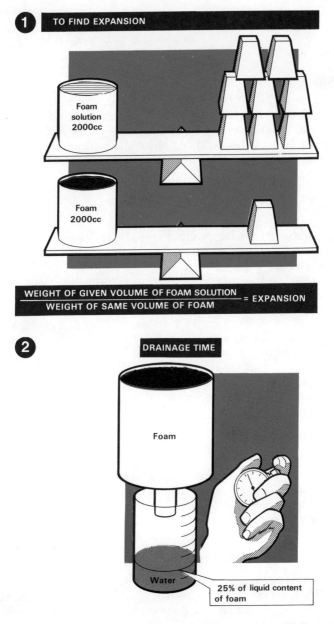

Fig. 9.1 Diagram showing tests to determine foam properties. (1) Expansion test. (2) Drainage time test.

Firemen should remember that, when a foam drains, its volume will seem almost unchanged. Although its integrity will appear good, its fire resistance will be low as it will have lost most of the water.

c. Shear stress

This is the degree of 'stiffness' of the foam, and it depends a lot on the size of the bubbles. A foam composed of small bubbles will be stiffer than one with large bubbles. This will obviously affect the flow of the foam, its ability to hold its liquid content (drainage time), and its resistance to breakdown and burn-back (security).

4 Storage of foam concentrates

The ability of a foam concentrate to be stored satisfactorily depends on its type and what sort of additives the manufacturer has included.

Protein-based concentrates store well provided they are not exposed to air. If this happens, oxidation may take place, causing a scum to form on the surface and then sink gradually to the bottom to form a sludge. This, of course, could cause blockages in the foam-making equipment, affecting the concentration and expansion of the foam.

All concentrates should be stored, and handled, in accordance with manufacturers' instructions. This applies to foam tankers and bulk storage tanks as well as container storage.

5 Compatibility of foam concentrates and foams

a. Concentrates

Different types and makes of foam concentrates are not always compatible, and manufacturers' advice and recommendations should be followed. The ground rules are mainly a matter of common sense, but a few points can be made as follows:

(i)   Do not mix together different types, or even brands, of concentrate in the same equipment.

(ii) When changing over from one type to another, especially in bulk storage or fire appliance tanks, first ensure that all of the old type is removed, and the tank and equipment thoroughly cleaned before refilling.

(iii) Depending on the age of the concentrate being replaced, even a new batch of the same brand might cause difficulties, and firemen should consult manufacturers if they are in any doubt.

b. Foams

Some foams will react unfavourably with certain fire extinguishing powders if used at the same incident. Here again, the manufacturer should be asked whether there are any particular incompatibles to his product. Firemen should remember to consult the industrial/MOD/CAA brigades etc. in their areas, as well as neighbouring local authority brigades where appropriate, to find out what types they are using.

Generally speaking, all types of finished foam can be used together on a single fire, although the order of application may affect their performance. For example, a non-aspirated film-forming foam or an alcohol-resistant type would obviously be better applied first if possible.

Chapter 10
Foam-making equipment

1 General

The aspirating devices which are used to produce foam can be divided into three basic categories:

(i)   foam-making branches (FMB) for LX or MX foam;

(ii)   generators for LX foam;

(iii) generators for HX foam.

The above equipment is available in various sizes requiring from under 100 l/min to over 6000 l/min of foam solution. It is obvious that pumps supplying water for foam-making must have the capacity to meet the needs of the particular type and amount of foam-making equipment in use.

Some aspirating devices are fitted with means of picking up concentrate and are known as *self-inducing*. With other types, the concentrate has to be introduced into the water stream at an earlier stage by some form of induction equipment. Methods of induction are described in more detail later.

2 LX foam-making branches

a. General

Fig. 10.1 illustrates the principal features of a typical LX FMB. Designs vary and will incorporate some or all of these features. The strainer is frequently omitted, as often is the on/off control.

In the diagram are two orifice plates. The upstream orifice is the larger of the two and its function is to create turbulence in the space between the two orifice plates so that when the jet issues from the downstream orifice it rapidly breaks up into a dense spray. This fills the narrow inlet section of the foam-making tube and entrains the maximum quantity of air through the air inlet holes. Some FMBs have the upstream orifice plate fitted with disturbance notches. The downstream orifice is smaller and is precisely calibrated to give the designed flow rate. Some branch-pipes have a swivel device in place of this orifice; others have several converging orifices.

Most FMBs have a narrow section at the inlet end in which the air entrainment takes place, and then a wider section in which

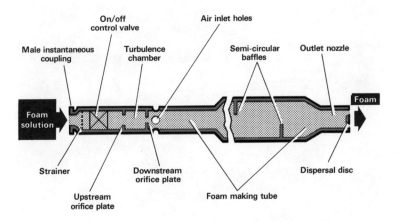

Fig. 10.1 Principal features of a low expansion foam branchpipe.

the foam forms. The wider section of the foam-making tube frequently contains 'improvers' which are designed to enhance the foam quality, e.g. semi-circular baffles or a cone.

At the outlet, the branchpipe is reduced in diameter to increase the exit velocity, thus helping the foam stream to be projected an

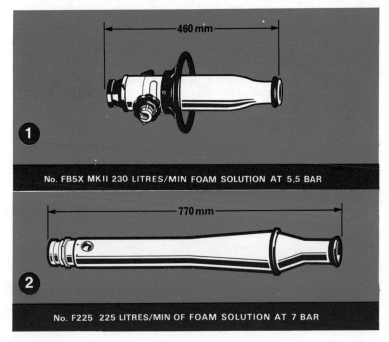

Fig. 10.2 LX foam branchpipes requiring approximately 225 litre/min foam solution.

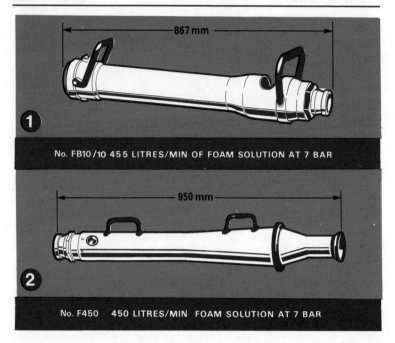

Fig. 10.3 LX foam branchpipes requiring approximately 450 litre/min foam solution.

effective distance. The design is crucial: too narrow an outlet produces back pressure with less air entrainment and a lower-expansion (sloppy) foam. If the outlet is too large, the expansion is higher but the throw is reduced.

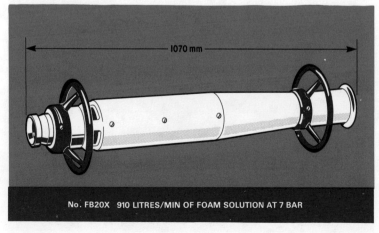

Fig. 10.4 LX foam branchpipe requiring approximately 900 litre/min foam solution.

Table 5

LX foam-making branches: performance data

Branch	Nominal flow require-ment (litres/min)	Nominal operating pressure (bar)	Maximum operating pressure (bar)	Throw at nominal pressure (metres)	Throw at maximum pressure (metres)	Expansion at nominal pressure (approx.)	Self-inducing capability	Remarks
FB 5X MkII	230	5.5	10.5	20	24	10:1	Yes	A recent development of the MkI. Can vary concen-tration from 3% to 6% when operated in self-inducing mode.
F 225	225	7	10	12[a] 20[b]	14[a] 23[b]	8:1[a] 10:1[b]	Yes	
B 225	225	7	8.8	13[c] 7[d]	14[c] 8[d]	10:1	No	Designed for use with film-forming foams. See page 65.
FB 10/10	455	7	10.5	21	25	10:1	No	Can change from straight-forward jet to conical spray.

Table 5—continued

LX foam-making branches: performance data

Branch	Nominal flow requirement (litres/min)	Nominal operating pressure (bar)	Maximum operating pressure (bar)	Throw at nominal pressure (metres)	Throw at maximum pressure (metres)	Expansion at nominal pressure (approx.)	Self-inducing capability	Remarks
F 450	450	7	10	18[a] 21[b]	20[a] 23[b]	8:1[a] 10:1[b]	Yes	
FB 20X	910	7	10.5	25	27	10:1	No	Requires 2 men to manoeuvre it. Often adapted as a monitor, either free-standing or fixed on an appliance.
F 900	900	7	10	21[a] 24[b]	23[a] 26[b]	8:1[a] 10:1[b]	No	Not illustrated, but similar in appearance to the F 450.

[a] Basic model, giving cohesive 'rope' type foam jet.
[b] Alternative version giving non-cohesive foam stream.
[c] Jaws open, i.e. jet mode.
[d] Jaws closed, i.e. spray mode.

Some branches are fitted with a dispersal mechanism, e.g. adjustable blades within the nozzle which enable a hollow conical spray to be produced. This overcomes the foam's tendency to remain in a coherent 'rope' and allows the foam to fall more gently onto the fuel.

b. Types

In order to distinguish between capacities of FMBs, it is necessary to use a common factor. As the same FMB can produce different amounts of foam from different concentrates, classification by foam production is useless. Therefore, the classification used in this chapter is by the nominal flow requirement of foam solution in litres/min. This figure corresponds in each case to the nominal operating pressure for the particular branch. Some common models of LX FMB are illustrated in Figs. 10.2 to 10.4, and their performance characteristics are listed in Table 5.

The B225 FMB (see Fig. 10.5) is specially designed for use with AFFF or FFFP, although it can be used with synthetic foam. Note the adjustable jaws giving the option of a cohesive jet or a spray, and the on/off trigger mechanism controlling the release of the foam. Table 5 gives the performance data for this branch.

Special types of branch are available for use with hose-reel equipment (see Section 7 below).

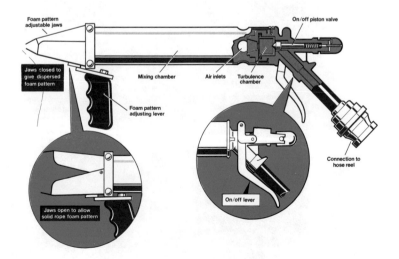

Fig. 10.5 The B225 spray/jet foam branchpipe for use with film-forming foams.

3 Foam monitors

Foam monitors are larger versions of FMB which cannot be hand-held. They may be free-standing and portable (Fig. 10.6 and Plate 1) or mounted on trailers (Fig. 10.7). They usually have multiple water connections, and may be self-inducing or use one of the induction methods described later. They can also be found as

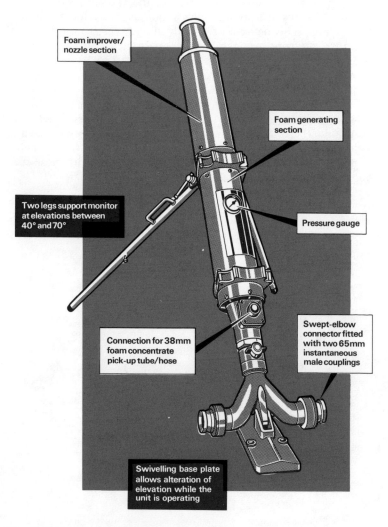

Foam improver/nozzle section

Foam generating section

Two legs support monitor at elevations between 40° and 70°

Pressure gauge

Swept-elbow connector fitted with two 65mm instantaneous male couplings

Connection for 38mm foam concentrate pick-up tube/hose

Swivelling base plate allows alteration of elevation while the unit is operating

Fig. 10.6 The Chubb 'Jetmaster' foam monitor.

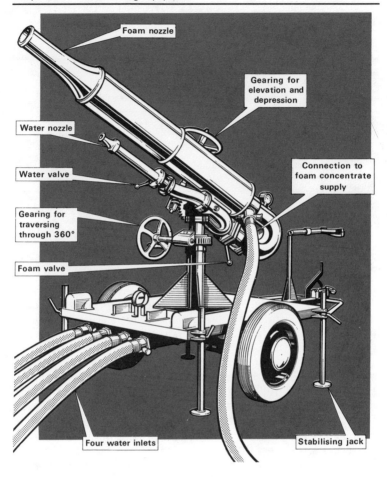

Fig. 10.7 Diagram showing the layout of a trailer-mounted foam monitor.

fixed installations at oil-tanker jetties and refineries (photograph, *Manual*, Book 4) or as oscillating monitors in aircraft hangars (see *Manual*, Book 4, Part 1). Similar monitors are fitted to airport foam tenders, and Plate 2 shows a typical example; note the adjustable jaws which allow the option of a flat fan-shaped spray. Some local authority brigade foam tenders are also fitted with a monitor.

Table 6 gives some performance figures for typical foam monitors.

Table 6

Foam monitors: performance data

Model	Nominal flow requirement (litres/min)	Nominal operating pressure (bar)	Length of throw (metres)	Height of throw (metres)
Angus FC 1800	2200	10	50[a]	20[b]
Angus FC 2700	3300	10	55[a]	22[b]
Angus FC 3600	4350	10	64[a]	24[b]
Chubb JetMaster	1680	10.5	40[c]	23[d]
Chubb Slimjet	3190	8	61[c]	24[d]

[a] 38° elevation   [c] 40° elevation
[b] 65° elevation   [d] 60° elevation

4 LX foam generators

As an alternative to a FMB, a LX foam generator may be used. This, when inserted in a line of hose, induces appropriate amounts of foam concentrate and air into the water stream to generate finished foam, which it then delivers through the hose to a water-type branch and nozzle. The foam concentrate is induced on the same principle as that of an inline inductor (see Section 8 below), and the air is drawn in through inlets adjacent to the water head (Figs. 10.8 and 10.9). The equipment can only work against limited back pressure, so the length and size of the hose between the generator and nozzle, and the size of the nozzle, are important.

Such generators are used to a limited extent in the Fire Service, the usual size being the No. 5A (Fig. 10.8). The recommended water inlet pressure of this model is 10.5 bar, and the nominal water requirement is 255 l/min. It can be used with up to 60 m of 70 mm hose, with a 38 mm nozzle. Larger sizes of generator are made but are generally in fixed installations.

5 MX foam-making branches

Medium expansion FMBs are generally designed to be used with synthetic foam concentrate and will produce foam at expansions usually ranging from 50:1 to 150:1. The greater expansion ratio of MX foam means that projection distances are far less than for LX.

With this type of branch, an inline inductor is used to introduce the foam concentrate—see Fig. 10.10. The branch then diffuses and aerates the stream of foam solution, and projects it through a gauze mesh to produce bubbles of a uniform size. The operating characteristics of some MX branches are shown in Table 7.

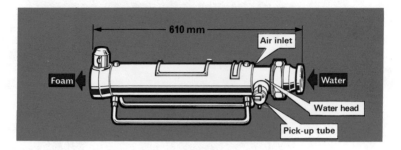

Fig. 10.8 Model 5A low expansion foam generator.

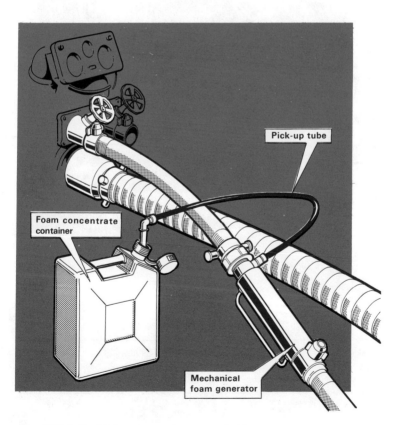

Fig. 10.9 A No 5A foam generator connected to a pump.

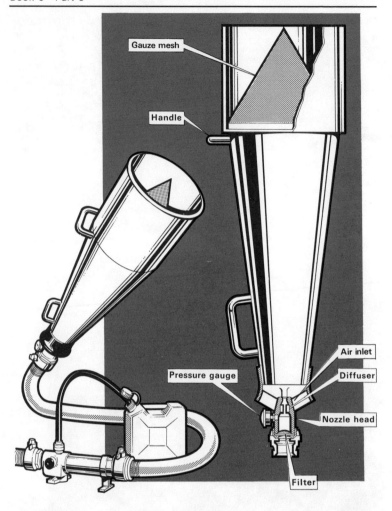

Fig. 10.10 Principle of operation of a medium expansion foam branchpipe.

Table 7

MX foam-making branches: performance data

Model	Nominal flow requirement (litres/min)	Nominal operating pressure (bar)	Expansion	Throw (metres)
MEX 225	170	2.5	65:1	7
KBM 50/60	225	5	60:1	7
KBM 50/150	225	5	150:1	3
MEX 450	300	2.5	65:1	8

6 HX foam generators

High expansion generators are designed to be used with synthetic foam concentrate (to JCDD/28 specification), and produce foam at expansion ratios usually from 200:1 to 1200:1.

Air is blown through the generator by a fan, a foam solution is sprayed into the air stream, and this is directed onto the surface of a fine net screen. This produces foam with a mass of bubbles of uniform size which is 'poured' rather than being 'projected'.

The generator fan may be powered by:

(a)   an internal combustion engine;

(b)   an electric motor; or

(c)   a water turbine which utilises the water used for the foam production.

Fig. 10.11 shows, in diagrammatic form, the essential principles of HX generators. Some generators require a separate inline inductor, but others are self-inducing and some can be operated either way.

Because the foam cannot be projected, it is usually fed to the fire through a large-diameter flexible tube. It can, however, be

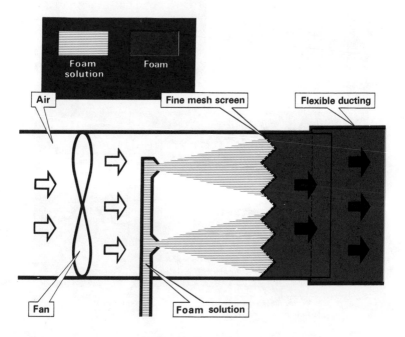

Fig. 10.11 Principle of operation of a high expansion foam generator.

used without ducting, e.g. placed on the side of a ship's hold or in a fixed installation in an aircraft hangar.

The larger HX generators use rather bulky equipment to carry on a first-line appliance, so they are usually brought on by a special vehicle (see Plates 8 and 9). However, recently some lightweight generators have been developed that can fit into a standard appliance locker. One example of the larger type is described below, together with notes on two lightweight models. All HX generators can be adapted for use as smoke extractors.

a. Angus Turbex Mark II

The Angus Turbex Mark II (Fig. 10.12) consists of a fan, driven direct from the shaft of a water turbine, which supplies an air stream to a nylon net. The net is wetted by foam solution from four spray nozzles which are supplied from the discharge of the turbine, the concentrate having been introduced into the water

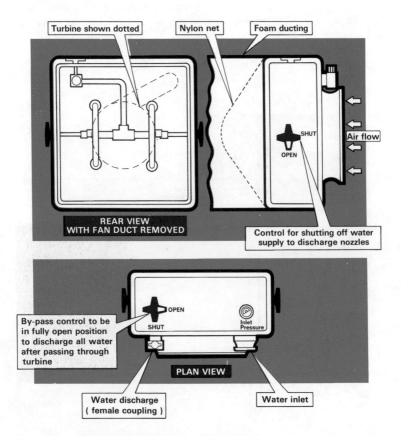

Fig. 10.12 Angus Turbex Mark II high expansion foam generator.

stream by a built-in induction system. The complete unit weighs 55 kg.

This generator incorporates a 'by-pass' system which allows it to operate against a high back pressure, e.g. when forcing foam through long lengths of ducting or up to a height.

With the by-pass closed, all the water passing through the generator is used both for driving the turbine and for foam production. This produces a lower-expansion foam containing a higher percentage of water. To overcome high back pressure the by-pass is opened, and some water is thereby diverted to pass through the turbine to waste, giving less for foam production. This results in a higher expansion ratio, with the foam having a lower percentage of water. It also slightly increases the water flow to the turbine, speeding up the fan and, consequently, the air flow.

The performance data of the Angus Turbex Mark II is given in Table 8. With by-pass closed, at 7 bar it will produce 133 m^3/min of finished foam.

Table 8

Angus Turbex Mark II: performance data

Mode of operation	Water inlet pressure (bar)	Total water flow (litres/min)	By-pass flow (litres/min)	Water used for making foam (litres/min)	Expansion
	4	170	60	110	800:1
	6	205	75	130	1000:1
By-pass fully open	7	225	85	140	1100:1
	8	240	90	150	1200:1
	10	265	95	170	1200:1
	4	160	Nil	160	500:1
	6	190		190	590:1
By-pass closed	7	210		210	640:1
	8	220		220	690:1
	10	250		250	760:1

b. Angus Mini-Turbex

Weighing about 16 kg, this much smaller water-turbine-powered generator (Fig. 10.13 and Plate 3) uses an inline inductor supplying premix solution. Table 9 gives performance data of the Mini-Turbex. At 7 bar this will produce about 80 m³/min of finished foam.

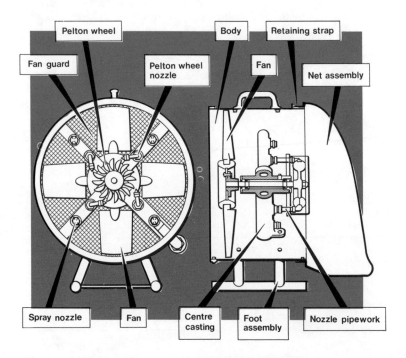

Fig. 10.13 Angus Mini-Turbex high expansion foam generator.

Table 9

Angus Mini-Turbex: performance data

Water inlet pressure (bar)	Water flow (litres/min)	Expansion
2.8	159	260:1
4.2	195	290:1
5.6	223	320:1
7.0	245	330:1
8.4	259	360:1

c. Chubb Fan-Hex 3000

Another of the smaller HX generators, weighing about 30 kg, this type is also supplied by an inline inductor. The operating pressure at the generator can range from 3.5 to 7 bar. At 5.25 bar, the water consumption is 205 l/min and foam output is 85 m³/min. This represents an expansion ratio of about 400:1.

7 Hose-reel foam systems

a. General

The effective 'knock-down' capability of many modern foams, particularly those of the film-forming type, has led to the development of systems for use with hose-reel equipment. The foam solution for this purpose may be pre-mixed in the appliance tank, or the concentrate may be induced by various methods. The foam may be delivered through some kind of special aspirating branchpipe; alternatively, a normal hose-reel branch may be used, with an aspirating tube clipped on if necessary. Two systems are briefly described below.

b. Galena 'Fog Foam' unit

The 'Fog Foam' is a small inline inductor which can be clipped in between the hose-reel tubing and the branch and has a third coupling set at right angles (Plate 4). To this can be coupled either:

(a)   a cylindrical magazine pre-filled with a 1% AFFF concentrate; or

(b)   a drum-fed pick-up tube. With this, the inductor is pre-set for 1, 3 or 6% concentrate as required.

A new magazine or pick-up tube can be fitted whilst pumping. The 'Fog Foam' is used in conjunction with a conventional hose-reel branch which produces non-aspirated foam. The foam solution requirement is 65 l/min at 7 bar (low-pressure model) or 26 bar (high-pressure model).

c. Chubb foam liquid proportioner

This is another development, consisting of a portable hand-held unit similar to an extinguisher (Fig. 10.14). It contains 11 litres of foam concentrate which can be either P, FP or AFFF. Any standard appliance hose-reel can be connected via an adaptor to the top of the unit and water supplied at between 2 and 10.5 bar.

A small proportion of the water is diverted to fill a completely deflated flexible bag within the container. Inflation of the bag displaces the foam concentrate via a syphon tube, the concentrate entering the main water stream and passing to an integral FMB to give a jet of aspirated foam.

With a water supply of 46 l/min at 3.5 bar, the unit will produce 360 l/min of finished foam. Control is exercised by a valve on the adaptor.

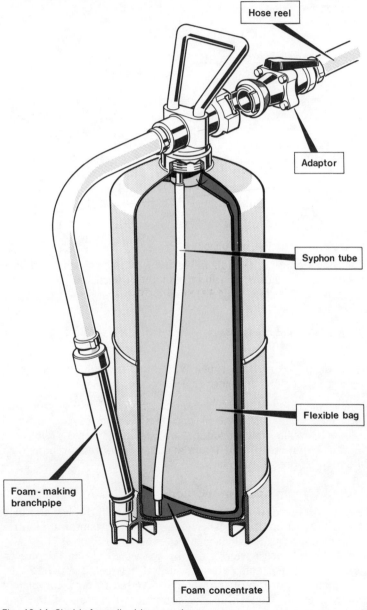

Fig. 10.14 Chubb foam liquid proportioner.

8 Foam concentrate inductors

a. General

As previously indicated, some FMBs are self-inducing and are fitted with connections enabling foam concentrate pick-up tubes to be used. However, this method of induction is not always satisfactory, for the following reasons:

(i)   Control and operation of the induction system is best carried out at a safe distance from the fire.

(ii) The FMB operator's movements are restricted if the branch is self-inducing.

(iii) Foam concentrate has to be transported to the branch.

For these reasons, most of the medium and large sized FMBs, and some of the smaller ones, use a system in which the concentrate is induced before the water reaches the branch. The two main items of equipment in use in the Service for this purpose are the *inline inductor* and the *round-the-pump proportioner*.

b. Inline inductors

An inline inductor (Fig. 10.15) is placed in a line of delivery hose usually not more than 60 m from the FMB. It uses the venturi principle, similarly to an ejector pump (see *Manual*, Book 7, Chapter 9), to induce the concentrate into the water stream. (NB Self-inducing FMBs also work in this way.) There will always be

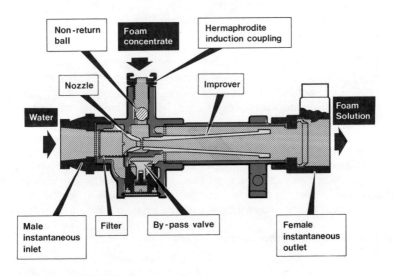

Fig. 10.15 Principle of operation of an inline inductor.

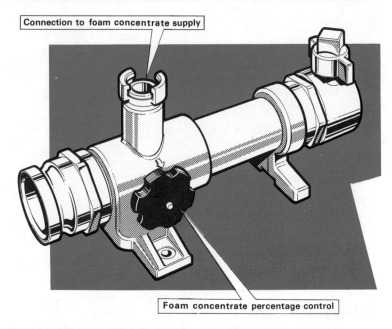

Fig. 10.16 An inline variable inductor.

a pressure drop across the inductor due partly to turbulence and partly to the energy loss involved in the induction.

In order for it to operate effectively, it is important to use an inductor with the correct throat size for the conditions. The crucial factor here is the volume of water passing through the system, and this depends on the nominal flow requirement of the FMB(s). Inductors and FMBs are therefore designed to 'marry up', e.g. an inductor designed for a flow of 450 l/min can be used with one FMB requiring 450 l/min or two requiring 225 l/min each. Typical sizes of inductor are 225 l/min, 450 l/min and 900 l/min.

Some inline inductors are variable, i.e. they have the additional facility of being able to vary the foam concentrate induction ratio, usually from 1% to 6%, by the operation of a control (Fig. 10.16).

Practically all inline inductors are designed to induce the foam concentrate through a pick-up tube placed in a drum or similar container. They can, however, be used in conjunction with a pressurised foam concentrate supply (see Section 10 below).

c. Round-the-pump proportioners

This type of inductor (Fig. 10.17) is connected across a pump and can either be a permanent fixture in the appliance or, with adaptors and connecting hoses, stand alone. It has a nominal

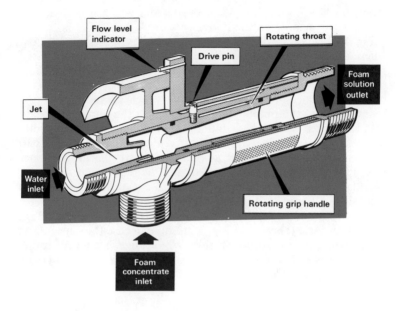

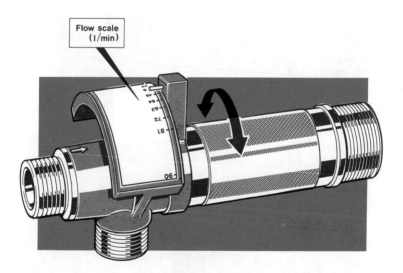

Fig. 10.17 A round-the-pump proportioner. Top: cutaway view. Bottom: external view.

induction flow range of 0–45 or 0–90 l/min which is varied by a rotating grip handle on the body.

Fig. 10.18 shows a typical round-the-pump proportioning system where an appliance has a built-in foam concentrate tank. When pumping begins, some water flows to the deliveries and some passes to the proportioner. The porportioner induces foam concentrate, to produce a rich foam solution which passes back to the suction side of the pump. Before re-entering the pump, the foam solution mixes with a fresh intake of water, and is consequently diluted to the required concentration. Most of it then passes to the deliveries, while a small amount returns to the proportioner where more concentrate is induced, and the sequence is repeated.

Isolating valves can be incorporated to cut off the system when foam is not required. Various other valves in this sort of system are incorporated to (a) drain the foam concentrate tank, (b) flush the system, and (c) connect a pick-up tube in case the concentrate tank is off the run. Although this proportioner has an operating pressure range of between 3 and 14 bar, the recommended pressure is 7 bar, with a water requirement of 193 l/min.

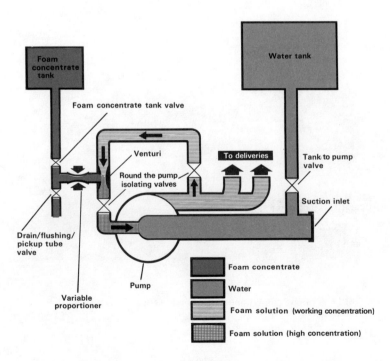

Fig. 10.18 Diagrammatic layout of a round-the-pump proportioner system where there is a built-in foam concentrate tank.

9 Pressure control valves

A round-the-pump proportioner will only function correctly if the pressure on the suction side of the pump is less than one-third of the pressure on the delivery side. If this limit is exceeded when pumping from a hydrant, the back pressure acting on the outlet of the proportioner will be sufficient to inhibit the induction of foam concentrate. To prevent this situation from arising, a pressure control valve may be used with the proportioner. The valve reduces the pressure in the pump inlet line to one-fifth of the hydrant pressure, thus bringing it within the required limit under any conditions likely to be encountered. The valve may be fitted as an integral part of the pipework system on an appliance, or used as a portable unit inserted into the pump inlet line at any convenient position.

Fig. 10.19 illustrates a typical pressure control valve. Water, under pressure from the hydrant, passes through the valve over a movable butterfly. This butterfly is connected to a hydraulic piston which receives pressure from both sides of the butterfly. The area of the piston subjected to pressure on the upstream side is one-fifth of the area of the piston on the downstream side, so the forces acting on the piston will balance when the downstream pressure is one-fifth of the upstream pressure.

If the upstream (i.e. hydrant) pressure increases, the downstream side will experience a proportionally greater pressure increase. This will immediately cause the piston to move, closing the butterfly and reducing the flow through the valve, thereby reducing the downstream pressure until the 5:1 ratio is restored. If the hydrant pressure falls, the reverse process will occur.

10 Pressurised foam concentrate supply

At a large incident requiring perhaps several large foam monitors, bulk supplies of foam concentrate from FoTs etc. will be required. In these circumstances, the conventional system of inducing the concentrate via a pick-up tube may be impractical, for the following reasons:

(i)   It may not be feasible to use foam concentrate drums to supply the inductor, because of the frequency with which they would have to be refilled.

(ii) The use of open-topped portable dams may not be entirely satisfactory, since the foam concentrate tends to aerate and this can interrupt the supply. Spillages can also occur.

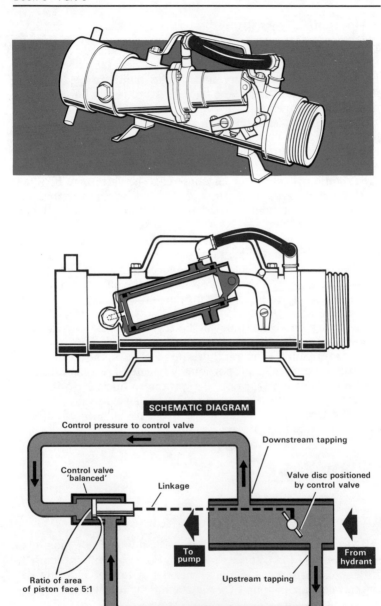

Fig. 10.19 A typical pressure control valve with cutaway drawing and schematic diagram..

(iii) Since the pick-up system requires the concentrate container to be positioned very near to the inductor, it may not be possible for a FoT to approach close enough to supply the inductor direct.

Even at smaller incidents, where it is practicable to use drums, there is the problem that it may be impossible to determine when the concentrate is about to run out. There could also be a danger of water being discharged onto the fire whilst the pick-up tube is being transferred when a container becomes empty.

To overcome these difficulties, a pressurised supply system has been developed, in which the foam concentrate is pumped from FoTs or bulk tanks to the induction points via hose lines (Figs. 10.20–10.22). FoTs normally have built-in pumps for this purpose.

Brigades have their different versions of this system, but they will all usually include some type of:

(a) distribution manifold, and

(b) metering devices.

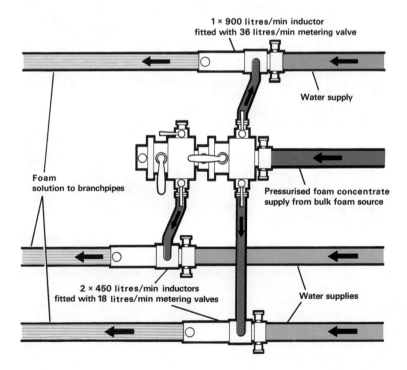

Fig. 10.20 Pressurised foam concentrate supply feeding 3 inline inductors.

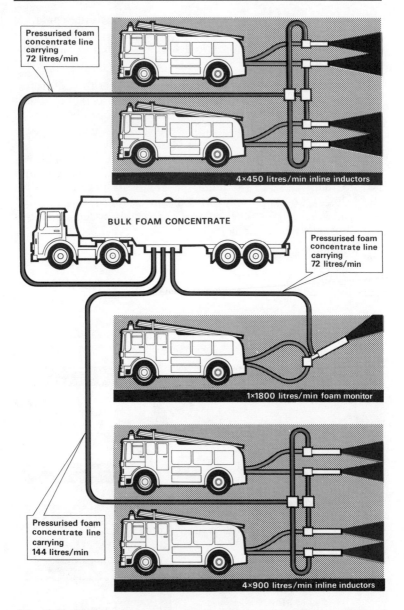

Fig. 10.21 Diagrammatic layout of an incident requiring large quantities of foam concentrate supplied from a bulk foam carrier.

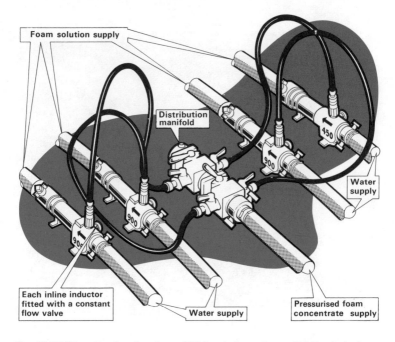

Fig. 10.22 Diagram showing three 900 litre/min and one 450 litre/min foam branchpipes receiving a pressurised foam concentrate supply from a foam tanker or foam main.

a. Distribution manifold

Various designs have been devised by brigades, some incorporating a metering device. Fig. 10.23 shows a typical distribution manifold which consists of a standard male instantaneous coupling leading to a manifold having two controlled outlets with 20 mm hermaphrodite couplings, one on each side, and a full-bore on/off valve. The manifold finally has a standard female instantaneous coupling at the other end.

This type of manifold is capable of feeding one or two inline inductors through 20 mm hose, each line passing up to 70 litres of foam concentrate per minute. If more than two inline inductors need to be used, a second manifold can be added to the first one, either directly (as, for example, in Fig. 10.22) or via additional lengths of hose. The shut-off valves on the manifolds are opened or closed according to the number of inline inductors to be supplied.

Plate 5 shows another example of a distribution manifold.

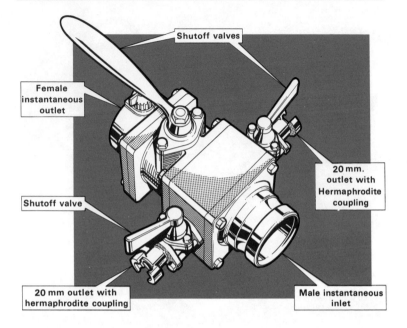

Fig. 10.23 A typical distribution manifold.

b. Metering devices

In order to ensure the optimum output of the monitors, the correct amount of foam concentrate should be fed to the inductors at all times. To ensure this, a metering device, or 'constant flow valve' as it is also known, is inserted into the line. Two types of metering device are described below.

(1) The Maric valve

In the Maric valve (Fig. 10.24), a flexible ring rests on a tapered seating. At low pressure the ring is fully expanded, giving the maximum orifice opening (Fig. 10.24, left). As the pressure rises, the ring is compressed and forced gradually down the tapered seating, progressively decreasing the size of the orifice (Fig. 10.24, right). The combination of increased pressure and decreased orifice size maintains a constant flow. A graph of the performance of a 4.5 l/min valve is shown in Fig. 10.25.

(2) The 'Mobrey constaflo' valve

In this valve (Fig. 10.26(1)) a neoprene diaphragm (shaped like a plug) is located above a profiled orifice. When subjected to pressure variations between 1 and 14 bar, this diaphragm flexes

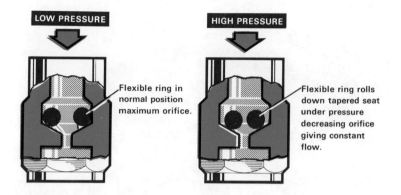

Fig. 10.24 Principle of operation of the Maric valve. Left: at low pressure. Right: at high pressure.

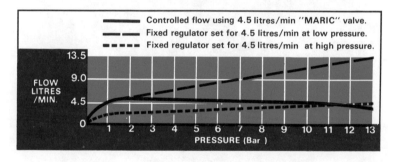

Fig. 10.25 Graph showing the performance of a 4.5 litre/min Maric valve.

onto the orifice, thereby increasing or decreasing the available orifice area and maintaining a constant rate of flow.

In Fig. 10.26(2), the cutaway drawing shows a multiple valve for high flow rates.

Plate 6 shows part of a foam tender with a Mobrey constaflo valve stowed in the top right-hand locker.

(3) Use of metering devices

These valves may be inserted at the inlet to each inline inductor or at some other point in the foam concentrate delivery line. Several brigades have had a foam monitor modified so that the valve is incorporated in the monitor. It is, of course, essential that a metering device of the correct flow rating for the equipment is used.

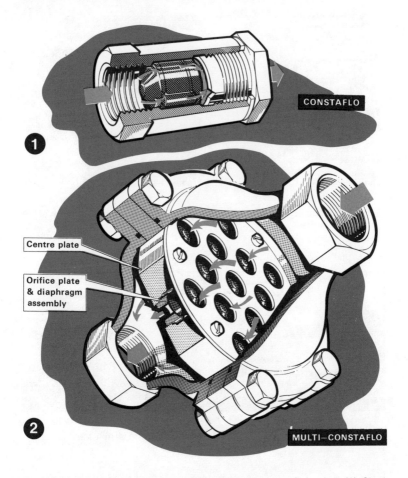

Fig. 10.26 Principle of operation of the 'Mobrey constaflo' valve. (1) Single valve. (2) Multiple valve.

11 Particular foam supply systems

At least two brigades are using demountable pod systems (Plates 7–9), each consisting of a foam tank divided into compartments, a fitted power unit and pump, plus accommodation for foam equipment and ancillary gear—all, of course, available to be picked up by a prime-mover. One brigade backs up its pods with a tank trailer unit with a capacity of 28,000 litres of foam concentrate (Plate 10).

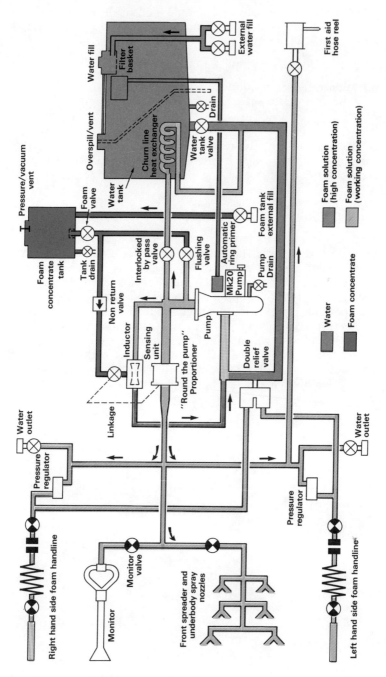

Fig. 10.27 Diagrammatic layout of the foam and water system of the Gloster Javelin airport foam tender.

Operationally the pods can be used individually or in series or, in one case, to make up a foam distribution ring main around the incident. Whatever system is envisaged, it must be:

(i)   relatively easy and quick to set up;

(ii)   under the strict control of designated officers (e.g. one per monitor plus a supervisor for the whole system);

(iii)   practised regularly.

If the tanks need to be refilled with concentrate from portable containers (barrels etc.), there should be a reliable system of lifting, positioning, discharging and removing the containers.

12 Specialised foam tenders

Airport foam tenders have to be able to produce large quantities of foam over a fairly short period. Some local authority brigade foam tenders also have the facility to produce large amounts of finished foam. Such high-capacity tenders usually employ a rather sophisticated type of round-the-pump proportioning system, often incorporating a pressurised foam concentrate supply. Besides being fitted with a large monitor, they will often have the facility of using hand-lines, which will have pressure regulatory systems controlling them. Fig. 10.27 shows the lay-out of the foam and water system of a Gloster Javelin airport foam tender. An illustration of such a vehicle is included in Book 4 of the *Manual*.

Chapter 11
Operational use of foam

1 General

Exactly how foam extinguishes a fire is difficult to assess, but the main factors appear to be:

(i)   formation of a sealing blanket over the fuel surface which prevents vapour escaping;

(ii)   interception of radiant heat from the flames, preventing it from reaching the surface of the fuel and causing further evaporation;

(iii)   isolation of the fuel from the oxygen in the air;

(iv)   cooling of the fuel;

(v)   dilution of the surrounding air with water vapour from evaporated foam.

It is obvious that the type of foam used and the method of applying it—i.e. non-aspirated or aspirated, LX, MX, HX—will largely dictate which of the above factors has the most effect on a particular fire.

2 LX foam

This is the most widely used type of foam because it

(i)   can be projected over fairly long distances;

(ii)   spreads fairly quickly;

(iii)   is capable of forming a stable and secure foam blanket.

a. Expansion and drainage requirements

Expansion rates are not usually greater than 15:1 and, to ensure that the finished foam blanket is 'secure' i.e. capable of resisting burn-back, minimum values of expansion and drainage time are usually prescribed. Typically these are an expansion of 5:1 and a drainage time of $1\frac{1}{2}$ to 2 minutes (as measured by the method described in Chapter 9). These values will depend on the foam type.

b. Applying the foam

(1) Rate of application

Minimum rates of application vary from 4 litres/m²/min to 6.5 litres/m²/min and depend a great deal on the fuel involved, the area of fuel burning and whether it is contained or free-flowing. Higher rates of application will be required for standard protein (P) foams than for FP, AFFF or FFFP, especially where fuels such as petrol are involved.

(2) Method of application

The normal application method is projection by foam-making branches but, in large tank fires, base-injection may be used. This may require an altogether different rate, mainly to overcome breakdown of the foam as it rises through the fuel.

LX foam should normally be applied gently to the surface of the burning fuel (or to the wall of the fuel container) to prevent the foam 'stirring' the fuel, which would contaminate the foam and thus reduce its capability to control the fire. Allowing the foam to spread across the burning surface is the best method. Any stubborn areas of fire should not be attacked directly but the surrounding blanket should be reinforced until it seals of its own accord. Plate 11 illustrates the ability of LX foam to spread over a large area.

The film-forming foams (AFFF, FFFP) may be applied in aspirated or non-aspirated forms. In the non-aspirated form they can be applied with standard water-delivering devices, even as a spray or fog. The expansion of non-aspirated foam is very low (of the order 2–3) and, under certain conditions and on certain fuels, it has a very quick extinction rate. It has drawbacks, however, in that it is not suitable for polar fuels or some of the more volatile hydrocarbons, has limited security in some circumstances and, when applied, may be invisible.

c. Oil-tank fires

The operational use of LX foam on oil-tank fires is discussed in detail in the *Manual, Part 6b, Chapter 5, Section 6,* but a few points can be commented on here.

(1) Preplanning

It is assumed that for every large oil refinery a lot of pre-planning has taken place. Equipment and material will have been earmarked, either on site or where readily mobilised. Table 10 gives some idea of the equipment, foam concentrate and water required to tackle hydrocarbon fires of various sizes. For example, a 60-minute supply of foam to a fire in a 90 m diameter tank needs almost 115 000 litres of concentrate and 1 800 000 litres of

Table 10

An example of quantities of resources and equipment required for major oil-tank fires

Diameter of tank (m)	Area of tank (m²)	Requirement (litres) per minute at application rate of 5 l/m²/min solution and 6% concentration			Requirement (litres) per hour (approx)			Quantity of equipment required (at recommended operating pressure)				
		Solution	Concentrate	Water	Solution	Concentrate	Water	225 l/min FMB	450 l/min FMB	900 l/min FMB	Jetmaster monitor	FC 3600 monitor
5	20	100	6	94	6000	360	5640	1	—	—	—	—
10	79	395	24	371	23700	1420	22280	2	1	—	—	—
15	177	885	53	832	53100	3185	49915	4	2	1	—	—
20	314	1570	95	1475	94200	5650	88550	7	4	2	1	—
25	491	2455	145	2310	147300	8840	138460	11	6	3	2	1
30	707	3535	210	3325	212000	12720	199280	16	8	4	3	1
40	1257	6285	375	5910	377000	22620	354380	—	14	7	4	2
50	1963	9815	590	9225	589000	35350	553650	—	—	11	6	3
60	2827	14135	850	13285	848000	50900	797100	—	—	16	9	4
70	3848	19240	1155	18085	1154000	69200	1084800	—	—	—	12	5
80	5027	25135	1510	23625	1508000	90500	1417500	—	—	—	15	6
90	6362	31810	1910	29900	1909000	114500	1794500	—	—	—	19	8
100	7854	39270	2355	36915	2356000	141400	2214600	—	—	—	24	10

water, using a 6% concentration and an application rate of 5 $1/m^2/min$ of foam solution.

A serious fire on a large tank requires the use of foam monitors. Some of the larger monitors used by brigades, or supplied by the oil companies, require over 4000 1/min of foam solution each, and there will usually be several of them at work.

It must be borne in mind that, although the area of the tank(s) is the main criterion in determining the resources and equipment needed, height is also a point to consider. A given area of burning fuel at ground level presents a very different problem to that of an equal area raised 20 m above the ground.

It is obvious that the pre-planning for large oil-tank fires must be very thorough as the logistics are extraordinary. The use of FoTs or other methods of bulk supply appears to be a first consideration.

(2) Firefighting

For large fires, the amount of equipment and material involved requires time to assemble in sufficient quantity to mount a sustained attack. In the meantime, cooling water jets and/or sprays should be applied to the surrounding area to prevent fire spread. Where supplies are limited, however, care should be taken to conserve enough water for the subsequent foam making.

The fire could have been burning for more than an hour before the foam attack starts, and two factors will have arisen during that time:

(i)   a large updraught caused by heated gases and inflowing air;

(ii) a very hot layer of fuel on, and near, the surface.

These immediately affect the foam application rate, which may have to be increased considerably. This in turn affects the amount of material available to sustain the attack for the planned time. The officer-in-charge may therefore have to delay the attack in order to muster more equipment and material, but he must bear in mind that such a delay will allow the tank to heat up further.

There is some argument about the application time for which it would be necessary to plan. Some authorities put it as low as 30 minutes, others 90 minutes. NFPA stipulate 60 mins. Large oil-tank fires do not occur often but a recent incident required some 700 000 litres of concentrate. In that instance the foam application lasted for several hours, and the logistical problems were formidable.

3 MX foam

Medium expansion foam gives substantially greater volume than LX but it flows less readily and can only be projected short distances. It has a moderate water retention capacity, and therefore moderate stability and heat resistance. The most common type of concentrate used is standard synthetic detergent, although FP and film-forming foams are now also being used for MX. HX concentrate can generally be used to produce MX in a MX foam branch.

An expansion of 60:1 is a typical value and MX is finding increasing uses. It is very useful for dealing with hydrocarbon spill fires and as a means of rapid vapour suppression and control e.g. on LNG, LPG and other cryogenic liquids. MX FP foam, applied gently, has been successful in controlling crude oil fires with long pre-burn times.

The Forestry Commission has experimented with the use of MX foam in laying a barrier to grass, heath and brush fires. Providing there is not too much wind, the foam remains in position and, besides the direct effect of stopping flames, the drainage helps to create a wet surface to impede any creeping fire. Application should be made not less than 5 minutes nor generally more than 60 minutes before the fire front hits the barrier.

4 HX foam

a. General

HX foam is produced from synthetic concentrate and the expansion ranges from 200:1 to 2000:1. Outputs are measured in cubic metres and a typical brigade HX generator can produce 200m³ per minute at an expansion of 1200:1. The foam is very slow-flowing and is poured rather than projected (see Chapter 10, Section 6). It is mainly intended for use in enclosed places. If, however, the wind conditions are light, it can be very effective outdoors for vapour suppression and, on the lower scale of expansion, e.g. 300:1 to 500:1, in controlling fires in spillages of hydrocarbon fuels. Its water retention, however, is limited and its stability and heat resistance are therefore less than those of lower-expansion foams.

b. Firefighting

HX is particularly suitable for dealing with fires in basements, ships' holds and machinery spaces, cable tunnels etc. Before foaming begins, the officer-in-charge must take time to get as much information as he can about the compartment he intends to flood, i.e. its nature, size, layout and contents. If the contents of the compartment are stacked or placed up to or near the ceiling, he must realise that the foam blanket may not extinguish all the fire, and be prepared to attack this later. He must bear in mind, however, that injection of HX foam will inhibit the use of any other firefighting technique and may make it more difficult to commit firemen into the compartment at a later stage.

An example of the use of HX foam can be seen in Plate 1 of Book 11 of the *Manual*.

(1) Foam concentrate requirement

If the size of the compartment can be ascertained, even on a rough basis, the officer-in-charge will be able to calculate approximately how much concentrate he needs to adequately fill it. To do this, he will need to know the approximate foam output of his particular HX generator in m^3/min at the required expansion, and its consumption of concentrate in litres/min. A simple table kept with the generator would help, but he must remember to allow for an initial fast breakdown of foam and the need to 'top-up' for a time.

(2) Siting of HX units

Generators should always, where possible, be placed in the open air, as products of the fire could otherwise affect foam volume and stability.

The discharge tube of the generator should be kept as short as possible, without kinks, and any opening used must be larger in cross-sectional area than the tube, to ensure that the maximum output can be generated. This all helps to cut down the back-pressure. Doorways, hatches etc. may be usable as they are, but, in some incidents, openings may have to be made or improved. There are various kinds of HX tubing, but a heat-resisting type must obviously be used if the conditions demand it.

(3) Level of injection

If HX foam can be injected at the floor level of the compartment, it will not have to contend with heated currents of air to penetrate the area. By the very circumstances of its use, however, it is nearly always injected at a higher level, and this will work provided that the injection is kept going steadily. There will probably be an initial fast breakdown but the sheer volume will soon penetrate.

(4) Ventilation

If a large volume of foam is to penetrate a compartment, it must displace the air in that compartment. Also, when the foam first attacks the fire a considerable amount of the water in it will flash to steam. All this, with the products of combustion, will result in a back-pressure which, if not ventilated, will physically prevent the injection of more foam.

One of the factors the officer-in-charge should have assessed is where he can ventilate the compartment safely. The best place will be diametrically opposite the generator(s), at the highest level. He may find that he has to block low-level openings and make suitable openings at a high level in order to ensure that the compartment is filled as quickly as possible. Opening up a ceiling or roof would be ideal, but in some cases the highest available opening may be several feet below the top of the compartment. To facilitate ventilation, smoke extractors could be employed in the openings; HX generators can be adapted for this purpose. The officer-in-charge must station crews with hand-controlled branches or hose-reels at all the ventilation openings to cover any fire which might appear there. Under no circumstances should any of this water be injected into the compartment, however, as this would break down the foam.

(5) Maintaining the foam

Changes in the colour of the smoke issuing from the fire will give a good indication of whether the foam is achieving control of the fire. As mentioned above, there will be a degree of breakdown of the foam, and an officer-in-charge should not, without good reason, stop injection until he is satisfied that he has the fire finally under control.

(6) Entering the compartment

All personnel entering a HX-filled compartment should wear BA, and the BA procedures should be rigorously applied. Firemen should take in a hose-reel or 45 mm hose line ready to extinguish with water any small pockets of fire still remaining, taking care that fire does not break out behind them.

(7) Hazards in HX foam

HX foam, even in a relatively well-known environment, has a very claustrophobic effect. In an unknown compartment this effect can be heightened, and other hazards encountered are:

(a) There is a general loss in effectiveness of vision, hearing and sense of direction, i.e. disorientation;

(b) penetration of light from torches and equipment is severely affected;

(c) audibility of speech, evacuation signals, low-pressure warning whistles and distress signal units is also restricted severely;

(d)   transmission of heat is reduced and the location and travel of fire are therefore harder to determine. Damage to structural features above and around may not be visible, with the danger of ceilings etc. collapsing onto firemen.

(e)   the compartment may contain trapped gases which, with the introduction of fresh oxygen, could produce minor flashovers;

(f)   openings, machinery, electric cables etc. will all be harder to discern, and progress must therefore be even more careful than usual. Guide lines and communications equipment should always be used if firemen need to be totally immersed in HX foam.

c. Clearing the foam

The removal of HX foam from a compartment is not easy. The Scientific Research and Development Branch (SRDB) have carried out tests with various methods and, of these, have recommended the use of:

(i)   a high-pressure hose-reel branch;

(ii)   a powder extinguisher; or

(iii)   a compact HX generator in suction, using semi-rigid ducting.

All these methods have disadvantages, and the operational situation will largely determine which method is used.

A high-pressure hose-reel is efficient but will cause further water damage. A powder extinguisher is also extremely efficient but leaves a combined powder/water residue which will have to be cleared by a salvage team. A compact generator is good, provided that the water residue is led away by hose and the ducting is not too long, but to clear all of a compartment the ducting will have to be moved around like a vacuum cleaner. This will be difficult where the compartment is large or where there is machinery, stacked goods, racks etc.

One obvious point which firemen should remember is that, the longer HX foam is left, the easier it is to break down. Drainage from the foam weakens the bubble walls and, in the tests using breakdown by water, it took less water to complete the job after a 30-minute interval than after a 15-minute interval.

Structure and publishing history of the *Manual of Firemanship*

The *Manual of Firemanship* was first published in a series of nine 'Parts' (1–5, 6a, 6b, 6c and 7) between 1943 and 1962.

In July 1974, it was decided that these nine Parts should be gradually replaced by 18 'Books' and a revised format for the *Manual* was drawn up. The new Books were to up-date the information given and arrange the subjects covered in more compact and coherent groups, each group occupying one of the new Books. The following pages show the original plan, *as amended to date*. Twelve of these Books have so far been published; the present volume is the second edition of Book 3.

Since 1974 there have been many developments in Fire Brigade practice and equipment and in the problems which firemen may have to face. To remain an authoritative and up-to-date survey of the science of firefighting the *Manual* must take these developments into account. Not all the necessary changes can be accommodated within the format announced in 1974. The reader should therefore be aware that the structure of unpublished Books of the Manual, as set out on the following pages is subject to change. Such changes will be publicised as far in advance as possible.

The next Book planned for publication is the second edition of Book 6: 'Breathing apparatus and resuscitation'. This should appear in the form described.

Manual of Firemanship

**Book 1 Elements of combustion and
extinction (published in 1974)**

	Formerly	
Part	*Part*	*Chapter*
1 Physics of combustion	*1*	*1*
2 Chemistry of combustion	*1*	*1*
3 Methods of extinguishing fire	*1 and*	*2*
	6a	*32 (III)*

**Book 2 Fire Brigade equipment (published
in 1974)**

	Formerly	
Part	*Part*	*Chapter*
1 Hose	*1*	*4*
2 Hose fittings	*1*	*5*
3 Ropes and lines, knots, slings, etc.	*1 and*	*7*
	6a	*39*
4 Small gear	*1*	*13*

**Book 3 (second edition) Hand pumps,
extinguishers and foam equipment
(published in 1988)**

	Formerly	
Part	*Part*	*Chapter*
1 Hand-operated pumps	*1*	*8*
2 Portable fire extinguishers and fire blankets	*1*	*9*
3 Foam and foam-making equipment	*1*	*10*

**Book 4 Incidents involving aircraft, shipping
and railways (published in 1985)**

	Formerly	
Part	*Part*	*Chapter*
1 Incidents involving aircraft	*6b*	*4*
2 Incidents involving shipping	*7*	*1–3*
3 Incidents involving railways	*6b*	*3*

**Book 5 Ladders and appliances (published in
1984)**

	Formerly	
Part	*Part*	*Chapter*
1 Extension ladders, hook ladders and roof ladders	*1*	*6*
2 Escapes	*2*	*3*
3 Turntable ladders	*2*	*4*
4 Hydraulic platforms	*2*	*5*
5 Special appliances	*2*	*6*
6 Pumping appliances	*2*	*1*

Book 6 (first edition) Breathing apparatus and resuscitation (published in 1974)

Part	Formerly Part	Chapter
1 Breathing apparatus	*1*	*11*
2 Operational procedure	*6a*	*32(V)*
3 Resuscitation	*1*	*12*

Book 6 (second edition) (not yet published)

Part	Formerly Part	Chapter
1 Breathing apparatus	*1*	*11*
2 Operational procedure	*6a*	*32(V)*
3 Protective clothing	—	—
4 Resuscitation	*1*	*12*

Book 7 (second edition) Hydraulics, pumps and pump operation (published in 1986)

Part	Formerly Part	Chapter
1 Hydraulics	*3*	*19*
2 Water supplies and hydrants	*3*	*20*
3 Pumps and pump operation	*2*	*1–2*
4 Water carrying and relaying	*3*	*21*
Appendices		

Book 8 Building construction and structural fire protection (published in 1975)

Part	Formerly Part	Chapter
1 Materials	*4*	*23*
2 Elements of structure	*4*	*23*
3 Building design	*4*	*23*

Book 9 Fire protection of buildings (published in 1977)

Part	Formerly Part	Chapter
1 Fire extinguishing systems	*4*	*24/26*
2 Fire alarm systems	*5*	*28*
3 Fire venting systems	*4*	*23*

Book 10 Fire Brigade communications (published in 1978)

Part	Formerly Part	Chapter
1 The public telephone system and its relationship to the Fire Service	*5*	*27*
2 Mobilising arrangements	*5*	*29*
3 Call-out and remote control systems	*5*	*30*
4 Radio	*5*	*31*
5 Automatic fire alarm signalling systems	*5*	*28*

Book 11 Practical firemanship I (published in 1981)

Part	Formerly Part	Chapter
1 Practical firefighting	*6a*	*32*
2 Methods of entry into buildings	*6a*	*35*
3 Control at a fire	*6a*	*33*

Book 12 Practical firemanship II (published in 1983)

Part	Formerly	
	Part	*Chapter*
1 Fire Service rescues	*6a*	*36*
2 Decontamination	—	—
3 Ventilation at fires	*6a*	*37*
4 Salvage	*6a*	*38*
5 After the incident	*6a*	*34*

Book 13
Contents not yet decided

Book 14 Special fires I (not yet published)

Part	Information available in		
	Part	*Chapter*	*Last edition*
1 Fires in animal and vegetable oils	*6c*	*45(8)*	*1970*
2 Fires in fats and waxes	*6c*	*45(3)*	*1970*
3 Fires in resins and gums	*6c*	*45(13)*	*1970*
4 Fires in grain, hops, etc.	*6c*	*45(6)*	*1970*
5 Fires in fibrous materials	*6c*	*45(4)*	*1970*
6 Fires in sugar	*6c*	*45(15)*	*1970*
7 Fires in paint and varnishes	*6c*	*45(9)*	*1970*

Book 15 Special fires II (not yet published)

Part	Information available in		
	Part	*Chapter*	*Last edition*
1 Fires in dusts	*6c*	*45(1)*	*1970*
2 Fires in explosives	*6c*	*45(2)*	*1970*
3 Fires in metals	*6c*	*45(7)*	*1970*
4 Fires in plastics	*6c*	*45(10)*	*1970*
5 Fires involving radioactive materials	*6c and*	*45(11)*	*1970*
	6a	*33(VI)*	*1971*
6 Fires in refrigeration plant	*6c*	*45(12)*	*1970*
7 Fires in rubber	*6c*	*45(14)*	*1970*

Book 16 Special fires III (not yet published)

Part	Information available in		
	Part	*Chapter*	*Last edition*
1 Fires in rural areas	*6b*	*1*	*1973*
2 Fires in electricity undertakings	*6b*	*3*	*1973*

Book 17 Special fires IV (not yet published)

Part	Information available in		
	Part	*Chapter*	*Last edition*
1 Fires in fuels	*6c*	*45(5)*	*1970*
2 Fires in oil refineries	*6b*	*5*	*1973*
3 Fires in gas works	*6b*	*2*	*1973*

Book 18
Contents not yet decided

Printed in the United Kingdom for HMSO
Dd292851 4/90 C50 G443 10170